CONTENTS

LOCAL AUTHORITY MEMBERS OF HELA

Association of Metropolitan Authorities

Mrs C M Moore
Association of Metropolitan Authorities

Mr W G Myers
(Joint Chairman and Local Authority Leader
of HELA)
Director of the Environment Department
London Borough of Hammersmith and Fulham

Mr D W Purchon
Director of Environmental Health and
Consumer Services
Sheffield City Council

Mrs J Russell
Environmental Services Manager
Kirklees Metropolitan Borough Council

Association of County Councils

Mr A Levitt
Deputy County Trading Standards Officer
Warwickshire County Council

Mr D McInnes
Association of County Councils

Mr E Clarke
Deputy Chief Fire Officer
North Yorkshire County Council

Association of District Councils

Mrs D Wood
Association of District Councils

Mr M R Garton
Principal Environmental Health Officer
Brighton Borough Council

Mr P D Wright
Director of Environmental Health
Watford Borough Council

Mr B Kember
Director of Environmental Health
Blaenau Gwent Borough Council

Mr P Lankester
Environmental Health Manager
Waverley Borough Council

Convention of Scottish Local Authorities

Ms M Dinsdale
Convention of Scottish Local Authorities

Mr D Henry
Director of Environmental Services
East Kilbride District Council

Mr J Smart
Director of Environmental Health
Perth and Kinross District Council

Mr G Bryceland
Director of Environmental Services
Monklands District Council

Mr M Drewry
Director of Trading Standards
Lothian Regional Council

Mr M Scott
Assistant Firemaster
Lothian and Borders Fire Brigade HQ

Former members of HELA - in post during 1991/92

Mr B Etheridge
Association of District Councils

Mr B Jones
Chief Environmental Health Officer
Torfaen Borough Council
Association of District Councils

Mr P C G Harris
County Trading Standards Officer
Surrey County Council
Association of County Councils

Mr M Eastwood
Director of Environmental Health
City of Manchester

Mr K Adams
Environmental Services Officer
Bournemouth Borough Council
Association of District Councils

Mr G Fish
Controller of Environmental and Consumer
  Services
London Borough of Barnet
Association of Metropolitan Authorities

Ms D McGiffen
Convention of Scottish Local Authorities

PREFACE

This is the third in the series of annual reports on local authority activity in administering the Health and Safety at Work etc Act. The series was inaugurated at a time when, as a result of recommendations by the Health and Safety Commission, local authorities were asked to assume responsibility for a substantial number of premises and activities, primarily in the leisure industries, which had previously been in the sectors administered by the Health and Safety Executive. This transfer added significantly to the classes of premises allocated to the local authority-administered sector since the implementation of the Act.

The recommendations were therefore an expression of the Commission's increasing confidence in the part played by the local authorities in health and safety matters; while at the same time both the Commission and the Executive were anxious to see an increasing convergence of standards and of priorities as between the authorities and as between them and the Executive in the way the Act was administered, recognising at the same time the autonomy of the authorities and the differences in the problems faced by each on the ground.

These reports to the Commission represent the principal channel of communication on these subjects. One of their key features are the statistical tables which have for the first time enabled authoritative comparisons to be made between the degree and type of hazard in each of the main areas administered by local authorities. These comparisons have already led to shifts in resources towards the higher risk areas and the higher action priorities, against the background of some decrease in the resources the authorities have been able to make available.

It is common ground between the Commission and Executive and the local authorities that effective preventative action in health and safety involves a concentration of activity on matters of the greatest importance and priority. The responsibility for health and safety under the law lies with the employer, and the primary aim is to assist and support her or his efforts. Inspection encourages and stimulates that responsibility and is not an end in itself and the use of powers, as Appendix 7 which sets out a common approach to enforcement explains, is a last resort applied for exemplary reasons, or on those whose disregard of the law is blatant or dangerous.

Such a policy depends on agreement and consultation on common standards, and the maximum information leading to a correct identification of the major priorities. We believe that this report breaks new ground in both these respects.

J McQuaid
W Myers
Co-Chairmen of HELA

FOREWORD

Sir J Cullen F Eng PhD
Chairman
Health and Safety Commission

We have been asked by the Health and Safety Executive/Local Authority Enforcement Liaison Committee (HELA) to present this report to the Commission on behalf of the local authorities that enforce health and safety legislation in Great Britain.

Local authorities have responsibility for the enforcement of health and safety in 1.2 million premises including offices, shops, retail and wholesale outlets, hotel and catering establishments, residential care homes and those in the leisure and consumer industry.

The report gives an insight into how local authorities have carried out their health and safety enforcement duties during 1991/92. It also explains how HELA is increasing its efforts to ensure a consistent approach to enforcement between HSE and local authorities and between the local authorities themselves. We believe this task to be of greater importance now that employers are faced with much new legislation from Europe.

Analysis of the health and safety supplement to the 1990 Labour Force Survey shows that we can no longer refer to many of the premises in the LA enforced sector as being low risk. Accident rates in many of the sectors are close to those in general manufacturing. Statistics indicate the majority of these accidents may be preventable, thus emphasising the importance of the local authority enforcement role.

Information supplied by local authorities indicates that they are responding positively to these concerns. Although the number of premises for which they have responsibility has increased, there has also been a significant increase in the number of visits made by local authority enforcement officers. The resources allocated to health and safety enforcement have fallen slightly, but effective targeting of visits has been further improved, thus ensuring they are directed primarily at those areas of highest risk.

The statistics in this report will enable priority planning systems to be refined, and the case studies in Part 2 should help in the prevention of accidents. These case studies contain information on the causes of accidents, the lessons to be learnt, and sources of futher advice. This should be of value to enforcers and employers alike.

We believe the information contained in the report will encourage local authorities to regularly review their resources for health and safety enforcement, thereby ensuring that adequate arrangements exist for this important area of work.

We recognise that many employers, particularly smaller ones, face genuine difficulties in familiarising themselves with the large body of new health and safety legislation which came into force on 1 January 1993. HELA's advice to local authorities on their approach to enforcement reflects this. It is consistent with HSE's policy, which has been well publicised. We have, therefore, followed the Commission's example and included details of our agreed enforcement policy in the report.

1992 saw two major changes for HELA. David Hodgkins relinquished the chairmanship on taking up a new post in HSE. HELA members have asked that this report records their appreciation of the contribution he made during his four years as Chairman, and they wish him every success in his new post. It was agreed that the opportunity would be taken to introduce a change in arrangements whereby the chair of the committee would be shared between local authorities and HSE. In consequence, Dr Jim McQuaid representing HSE and Bill Myers representing local authorities took over as Joint Chairmen.

Our Plan of Work for the forthcoming year recognises the importance which you and the Commission attach to health and safety management and training. We hope this will strengthen even further the partnership between HSE and local authorities.

Dr Jim McQuaid

William G Myers

SUMMARY

This report of the Health and Safety Executive/Local Authority Enforcement Liaison Committee (HELA) is made on behalf of the local authorities which enforce health and safety legislation and the relevant statutory provisions in Great Britain.

The report is in three parts. Part 1 gives an insight into the ways in which local authorities are carrying out their health and safety enforcement duties. It also describes some of the work done by HELA and its sub-committees. Part 2 contains case studies of some fatal accidents which occurred in the LA enforced sector, and special studies of accidents in retail, hotel and catering, and the leisure industry. Part 3 provides accident statistics and analysis, together with information about LA enforcement activity and trends. It is based on accidents reported to local authorities under the Reporting of Injuries, Diseases and Dangerous Occurrences Regulations 1985 (RIDDOR) and on returns from 404 local authorities. Part 3 also looks in detail at injuries in retail, hotel and catering and food handling, and provides further information on risks to part-time employees from the Labour Force Survey carried out in 1990. Parts 2 and 3 are based on data relating to the year 1/4/91-31/3/92. Part 1 covers from 1/4/91 to the time of writing.

Local authorities enforce health and safety legislation across a large and diverse range of activities in the services sector, many of which have a high level of public access. They became responsible for an additional 80 000 premises during the year. Nearly a third were in the consumer/leisure services sector, and this reflects a continuation of the realignment of enforcement allocation under the 1989 Enforcing Authority Regulations. Last year's report included details of results obtained from the analysis of a supplement to the 1990 Labour Force Survey. This indicated a lower than expected level of reporting of accidents in the local authority sector. The rate of accidents was, therefore, higher than previously thought. Further analysis, looking specifically at the influence of part-time working, showed the accident rate to be even higher, approaching that of manufacturing. This emphasises the importance of the work of local authorities in the enforcement of health and safety legislation.

This year's report shows that local authorities have continued to improve on their efficient use of staff resources. There has been a rise in the number of visits made by each full time equivalent member of staff. Local authorities have also continued to plan their visits more effectively, giving greater attention to those premises of higher risk. The number of visits to catering and retail premises have increased by 13% and 5% respectively, while visits to lower risk premises, such as offices, have decreased. This most encouraging sign demonstrates that greater use is being made of priority planning and inspection rating systems.

Enforcement action taken by inspectors continues to increase. Compared with 1990/91, prosecution hearings rose by 18% and the number of notices issued increased by 66%. While the increase may reflect more serious breaches of health and safety legislation, the impact of the transfer of higher risk activities, such as those found in the leisure industry, and the targeting of higher risk premises, will have had an effect. Comments by the Audit Commission must also have influenced attitudes to enforcement action. In its report on the management of environmental services *Towards a Healthier Environment* the Audit Commission noted that "there was a growing body of argument for the effectiveness of rigorous enforcement, often by prosecution at an early stage". It also stated that a determined prosecution strategy has considerable merit in management terms. The heightened attention to enforcement action associated with the Food Safety Act will also have had some influence.

The new European based legislation represents a major challenge to employers and enforcers alike. During negotiations in Europe HSE's representatives were successful in ensuring that many Directives were brought more into line with existing UK policy and practice. However, the volume of legislation is such that many will face real difficulties in familiarising themselves with the new law. Local authorities recognise this and HELA has endorsed HSE's approach to enforcement, ie in the period immediately after the coming into force of the new Regulations, inspectors will promote awareness of the Regulations and point employers in the direction of sources of advice and guidance. Formal enforcement measures are not likely unless the risks to health and safety are evident and immediate, or what needs to be done is not new, or employers appear deliberately unwilling to recognise their responsibilities.

There is a need to ensure that the nature of enforcement is clearly understood and, particularly, that it is aimed at preventing accidents and ill health, rather than just punishing offenders after an incident. The current Review of Regulation by the Health and Safety Commission may affect future enforcement policy, but promoting consistency of enforcement is essential. Therefore, this report is following the lead set by the Health and Safety Commission in their last report by devoting a special appendix to the subject.

The volume of new law has also caused local authorities and HSE to look more closely at the training needs of local authority enforcement officers. Training links have been improved to ensure even better consistency of enforcement. HELA is aware that working with local authorities to ensure properly co-ordinated enforcement of the new EC led requirements remains a priority of the Health and Safety Commission.

The report is the first to indicate that local authorities may now be beginning to attach greater importance to health and safety at work. HELA will continue to encourage this process.

Local authorities continue to work in partnership with HSE, in enforcing health and safety legislation. During 1991/92 the enforcement statistics show that:

- 1 230 000 premises were the responsibility of local authorities for enforcement, an increase of some 7% over the number for 1990/91;

- of the 80 000 extra premises 25 000 were in the consumer and leisure services sector, reflecting the continuing transfer under the Enforcing Authority Regulations and local authorities' continuing work to seek out new premises;

- the number of full time equivalent staff in local authorities enforcing health and safety is sligtly lower than in 1990/91;

- there was a large increase in the number of enforcement notices issued, up by 66% on 1990/91;

- 514 prosecution hearings were completed, an increase of 18% on the previous year;

- for the second year running, the number of visits made by LA inspectors rose, 6% on 1990/91;

- local authorities have handled the increase in premises by more efficient use of resources and exercising priority inspection. This has resulted in visit rates to higher risk premises being maintained;

The main points arising from the accident statistics for 1991/92 are:

- 24 205 injuries were reported to local authorities. Of those, 4331 were major injuries and 62 were fatal;

- there were 1935 major injuries to members of the public and 32 fatal injuries;

- the rate of major injuries to employees shows no real trend;

- the highest rates of major injury to employees are in the recreational and wholesale sectors;

- the highest rates of over-3-day injury are in retail distribution and social welfare;

- slips trips and falls on the same level and falls from a height accounted for about two-fifths of all injuries and three-quarters of major injuries;

- handling, lifting and carrying accounted for 27% of all injuries.

During the past six years the rate of over-3-day injury has risen substantially in all main industries of the local authority sector. This appears to reflect worsening performance rather than better reporting of injuries.

The report includes further analysis of the 1990 Labour Force Survey:

- the extent of under-reporting of injuries and the level of part-time working in the services industries means that previous estimates of the rates of injury were substantially understated;

- work in retail, wholesale and hotel industries has over four-fifths of the accident rate in manufacturing as a whole.

1 LOCAL AUTHORITY ENFORCEMENT

Introduction

1   The Health and Safety at Work etc Act 1974, and regulations made under it, are enforced by the Health and Safety Executive (HSE) or by local authorities (LAs), according to the main activity carried on at individual premises.

2   The Act itself does not set out which premises fall to HSE and the local authorities, but section 18 enables regulations to be made which allocate particular types of premises to local authorities. Such regulations (the Health and Safety (Enforcing Authority) Regulations) were first made in 1977. Further regulations made in 1989 resulted in the reallocation of an estimated 120 000 additional premises from HSE to local authorities from 1 April 1990. Full details of the enforcement arrangements and responsibilities of local authorities are given in Appendix Five.

3   In recognition of public concern that legislation should be enforced in a consistent way, special arrangements have been established to provide effective liaison between HSE and local authorities, both at national and local level. The arrangements also ensure that the policies of the Health and Safety Commission (HSC) and the technical guidance available in HSE are brought to the attention of all local authorities. These arrangements comprise: a joint liaison committee operating at national level, the Health and Safety Executive/Local Authority Enforcement Liaison Committee (HELA); a Local Authority Unit (LAU) in HSE; and an Enforcement Liaison Officer (ELO) operating at the local level in each of HSE's Area Offices.

4   This part of the report starts by describing some of the work done by HELA and its sub-committees. It then describes the way in which some local authorities have responded to the challenge of improving the protection of people at work and the public and deals with other areas of particular interest. Finally, it addresses the concerns of local authorities and gives a view of the way forward. Part 1 covers the period from 1 April 1991 up until the time of writing. Parts 2 and 3, which deal with accidents and statistical data, relate to the year 1 April 1991 to 31 March 1992.

Liaison arrangements

HEALTH AND SAFETY EXECUTIVE/LOCAL AUTHORITY ENFORCEMENT LIAISON COMMITTEE (HELA)

5   HELA is responsible for the overall formulation and direction of policy and activity concerned with the interface between HSE and local authorities as the enforcers of health and safety legislation. Background information on HELA and its sub-committees is given at Appendix 6. HELA prepares this report on health and safety in the service industries and submits it to the HSC on behalf of the local authorities. It also approves and submits to the HSC a plan of work for the HSE's Local Authority Unit. Detailed work is carried out through HELA's five sub-committees. The following paragraphs set out some of the work undertaken.

6   One of the main tasks facing this sub-committee was that of providing assistance to local authorities in the training of their enforcement officers in the requirements of the six new sets of health and safety Regulations which came into force on 1/1/93. The Regulations implement a series of European Directives from the EC's Social Action Programme. In EC negotiations HSE aims to minimise burdens on business and its representatives have been able to achieve substantial improvements to the original proposals made by the European Commission. These have brought the Directives more into line with existing UK policy and practice. Nevertheless, the volume of new legislation was recognised as presenting a major challenge to employers and to HSE and LA inspectors.

7   Consistency of enforcement between HSE and local authorities can only be achieved if there is also consistency in training. Therefore, THELA reached agreement with the training section of HSE's Field Operations Division that a group of nominated local authority representatives be invited to attend a series of seminars on the new Regulations for all HSE inspectors. A major thrust of these seminars was to reinforce the importance of a reasonable approach to enforcement. These representatives, who had been given access to all the relevant HSE training material, were then able to provide cascade training for other local authority enforcement officers at venues arranged through the Institution of Environmental Health Officers, (IEHO), and the Royal Environmental Health Institute of Scotland, (REHIS). In addition, further local authority enforcement officers were invited to the seminars on an ad hoc basis. At the same time advice on HSE's general enforcement policy for the new legislation was sent to all local authorities in a letter from Mr Bill Myers, Local Authority Leader and Joint Chairman of HELA.

8   One of the main functions of THELA is to facilitate the production of open learning courses. The Local Authority Unit has overseen the production of four of these and two more, one on noise and one on pressure systems are in hand. It is also intended to start work as soon as possible on two more courses, the first of which will deal with the legislation on display screen equipment. This subject has been chosen from the six new sets of Regulations as it is particularly relevant to the LA enforced sector.

9   Originally the open learning courses were aimed at local authority enforcement officers. However, experience has shown they have also been welcomed by employers and others, including HSE's own inspectors, and future courses will take this into account. In addition, the committee is liaising closely with that part of HSE which develops open learning courses for its own inspectors, to ensure that, where applicable, the local authority enforced sector is included. An example is a document on the storage of liquefied petroleum gas which is due to be published in 1993.

10   Because of the heavy commitment to this type of training material, THELA recommended that the initial courses be fully evaluated to ensure they were meeting the needs of customers. The primary customer was taken to be the local authority enforcement officer, although the views of HSE inspectors and employers were taken into account.

11   The evaluation was carried out by Andrew Georgiou, an Environmental Health Technician from Sefton Borough Council, who joined LAU on a 2 month secondment. The methodology used was developed in consultation with HSE's Statistical Services Unit to ensure that the results were valid. A number of objectives were defined and it was agreed that a series of questions would be directed at a

random sample of local authority enforcement officers (involving nearly 100 LAs in total). The questions were piloted and refined as necessary.

12   Feedback from the main target audience confirmed that open learning courses were considered to be both suitable and effective as a training medium. However, it was acknowledged that maximum benefit could only be achieved if the courses were used in the correct way. Sufficient time needs to be made available, along with additional tutoring where necessary. Users felt that the quality of the material was good. All recommendations on improvements were discussed with the writers.

13   The committee acknowledges that evaluation needs to be ongoing and, therefore, all future open learning courses will incorporate an evaluation sheet. It is important that users take the time and trouble to complete these. The committee will continue to maintain an open mind on training to ensure the most effective medium is always used.

14   Although PHELA (see paragraph 15) deals with most aspects of pesticides work, THELA was asked if it could assist in the provision of direct training for local authority enforcement officers by HSE staff who already had extensive enforcement experience of the pesticides legislation. HSE's Field Operations Division agreed to offer the services of a number of its staff from the Agricultural Inspectorate, who spoke at several venues across the country. These talks were organised through the REHIS and IEHO networks. A similar exercise was carried out with the Institute of Trading Standards Administration (ITSA), who represent trading standards officers (TSOs). TSOs have responsibility for the commercial and consumer aspects of the pesticide legislation relating to advertising sale and supply. In all, some 500 inspectors have received this training, which is still ongoing.

PESTICIDES SUB-COMMITTEE (PHELA)

15   The Food and Environment Protection Act 1985 (FEPA) and the Control of Pesticides Regulations 1986 (COPR) control the marketing, storage and use of pesticides in Great Britain. This legislation has been enforced by HSE since 1987, but there was no local authority involvement in the enforcement of its requirements until April 1992.

16   The concept behind the development of the policy for enforcement of pesticides legislation was that businesses should not be burdened with enforcement of related legislation by different officers. On this basis it was proposed that in Great Britain the enforcement of FEPA/COPR would be allocated in a way which reflected the existing divisions of responsibility between HSE and LAs on the enforcement of the Health and Safety at Work etc Act 1974.

17   With the prospect of an expansion of the number of people involved in enforcement, the Ministry of Agriculture, Fisheries and Food (MAFF) was concerned there should be a consistent approach to enforcement and that local authority enforcement officers should be trained and supported in their enforcement activity. They were aware of HSE's arrangement for liaison with local authorities on enforcement of the HSW Act through HELA and negotiated with them to use HELA for liaison on FEPA.

18   HELA recognised the areas of similarity between FEPA and HSW Act and the advantages to LAs of being able to discuss and resolve problems of common interest with other enforcing agencies and having advice on technical and enforcement questions in a format with which they were already familiar. HELA

therefore agreed to the establishment of the PHELA sub-committee. Administrative support for PHELA was put in place in June 1991 and the committee established in September of that year.

19   A hectic period of preparation ensued during which an open learning course and some 16 circulars (HELA LAC Pesticides) were produced, providing foundation blocks of guidance on various aspects of the legislation.

20   It is too early to report on the effects of LA involvement in enforcement of FEPA/COPR requirements. However, if the positive feedback to LAU can be taken as an indication of the priority LAs are giving to the enforcement of the legislation, then the years 1992/1993 should provide some interesting facts about the marketing, storage and use of pesticides in the LA enforced sector.

STANDARDS OF COMPLIANCE SUB-COMMITTEE (SCHELA)

21   SCHELA members continued to support HELA by developing guidance for local authority enforcement officers in areas where enforcement issues had been shown to require clarification. Many of these issues have arisen as a result of uncertainty over the allocation of premises but there has been a marked increase in the requests for advice on health and safety aspects associated with the leisure industry, which was transferred to local authority enforcement in April 1990. This is particularly the case with the novel forms of "participant entertainment" such as bungee jumping and bar-fly jumping but is also the case with more established spectator sports such as motor sport.

22   The sub-committee oversees the production of the guidance project in which a local authority inspector joins HSE on a 6 month secondment to write guidance on a specific topic. The topics are agreed by HELA and reflect the concerns of local authorities, accident and ill-health records and the views of employers/employees organisations. A report on the guidance project is given in paragraphs 89-92.

23   Members were regularly consulted on the likely impact of new legislative proposals,in particular the Registration of Cooling Towers Regulations as a further means to control Legionellosis. Comments were also made on the six draft Regulations based on European Directives.

24   Surveys to assess the impact of the Noise at Work Regulations were carried out with local authority support and SCHELA helped to arrange for data to be collected by local authorities on fork-lift truck training, electrical accidents and violence at work.

25   Guidance on health and safety in circuses was also considered by SCHELA. This was originally planned as a technical circular for local authorities with a data sheet for employers but is now to be published. The Home Office have agreed to provide a section covering fire precautions. The target date for publication is mid-1993.

STATISTICS SUB-COMMITTEE (SHELA)

26   SHELA has continued to support HELA in relation to its responsibilities for the database for LA enforcement of health and safety legislation and for the oversight of the production of this annual report. The principal work of the sub-committee has involved keeping under review the data obtained through the local authority annual returns (Forms LAE 1) and their analysis. It is these data which form

the core of the annual report to the Health and Safety Commission and provide the necessary support to LAs for their priority planning purposes. The form itself was reviewed by a working group. They completed their work in less than 5 months and further information on the outcome of the review is given in paragraphs 76-83.

27 The number of LAE 1 returns remains at around the 400 mark and HELA is very appreciative of the co-operation of all those authorities which provide this vital information each year, without it this annual report would not be possible. However, it would make this report even more complete if the remaining 60 or so LAs which make no return would do so.

28 The commencement of the review of RIDDOR was mentioned in last year's report and SHELA has had an important part to play in that review (see also paragraphs 160-167). In addition to seeking SHELA's, other sub committee's and HELA's views, seven LAs were visited as part of the review. They all expressed concern about under reporting of accidents; the existing format of the accident report form, in that it did not facilitate the giving of adequate information on the cause of accidents; and the requirement to report within 7 days, feeling that 10 days would be more appropriate. They were also concerned about the problems of dealing with accidents involving delivery drivers based outside an LA's area.

29 At the beginning of the year the Royal Environmental Health Institute of Scotland (REHIS) joined the IEHO as observers on the sub-committee.

EUROPEAN SUB-COMMITTEE (EUROHELA)

30 The EUROHELA sub-committee continued the task it began in 1991 of advising HELA on the policy implications of proposals made by European institutions as they affect the enforcement of health and safety legislation by local authorities. The sub-committee is concerned with proposals for directives or standards. Once a proposal has been agreed, detailed comment on the draft Regulations to implement the directive is the responsibility of SCHELA.

31 Attention has naturally been concentrated on the six main Directives on Workplace Safety, Manual Handling, Display Screen Equipment, Provision and Use of Work Equipment, Personal Protective Equipment, and Management of Health and Safety at Work, but members also discussed proposals concerning Construction, Young Persons, Agriculture and related workplaces, and Asbestos.

32 The sub-committee became involved in the early planning for the European Year of Safety, Health and Hygiene and local authorities were among the most active supporters of projects and proposals to mark the year. See paragraphs 154-159.

HELA and LAU liaison with industry and other bodies

33 Relationships with industry have strengthened, building upon the links developed over the last 3 years. The meetings with the British Retail Consortium (BRC) have continued to provide an important dialogue on health and safety policy and enforcement issues. This has proved particularly valuable in consultation on the EC Directives dealing with health and safety, and in looking at the issue of

violence in the retail sector. The BRC showed substantial interest in the Lead Authority Pilot Project reported on elsewhere in this report. (See paragraphs 119-130).

34   Meetings were also held with the Health and Safety Committee of the Brewers' Society and the British Soft Drinks Federation. The LAU was represented at meetings with the Banks and Building Societies on health and safety matters and liaison with the food industry through the Food National Industry Group has developed into the formation of a committee representing catering interests.

35   A further meeting has been held with trade unions representing employees in the LA enforced sector. These meetings have become a regular feature and they serve to inform unions about the work of LAU and HELA in the increasingly important LA enforced sector.

36   These contacts with the wide range of industry and business interests which make up the services sector, are essential to inform HELA's deliberations and the work done on its behalf.

37   Meetings have been held with the Local Authority Associations and consumer interest groups, both to inform them of current and planned work and to provide direct feedback on the effectiveness of HELA's activities. HELA continues to keep in close touch with professional institutions and associations representing local authority inspectors' interests and the LAU is represented on the Health and Safety Co-ordinating Groups (HASCOG) operating both in England and Wales and in Scotland. The LAU with other parts of HSE continue to be strongly represented at the annual conferences of IEHO, REHIS and the Institution of Safety and Public Protection (ISPP) and have developed a high profile at the associated exhibitions. Collectively they attract more than 1500 delegates from the LAs.

SEMINAR ON HEALTH AND SAFETY IN THE RETAIL SECTOR

38   During the year, an important development took place in the growth of co-operation and co-ordination on health and safety enforcement. A one day seminar, organised jointly by LAU, British Retail Consortium and the IEHO, was held on key health and safety issues in the retail sector. The importance of good communication between regulators and industry is increasingly being stressed and this seminar, which brought together representatives of industry and enforcing authorities, has given a positive lead for the future.

39   The event was attended by safety officers and managers with responsibility for health and safety from a wide range of companies and by senior local authority enforcement officers. It provided delegates with information on European health and safety initiatives, including the Framework Directive and the Manual Handling Directive, and gave them an opportunity to discuss these developments and other issues relevant to retail services, including violence to staff. The seminar also gave delegates an opportunity to consider their role in maintaining and improving health and safety standards.

40   The response to the event was favourable and it is planned to hold a further joint HSE/BRC/IEHO seminar in 1993. This is likely to focus on the practical implications for the retail trade of the six new sets of Regulations which have implemented the EC Framework and its subsidiary Directives, along with other topical issues.

41 The term enforcement covers a whole range of activities from advice through to legal proceedings. The following entries illustrate how various local authorities have approached enforcement.

ENFORCEMENT POLICY

42 The City of Glasgow District Council decided that their main priority was to ensure enforcement work was carried out in an efficient and effective manner. A review was therefore undertaken of the enforcement techniques currently in use. The review recognised the need to alter existing enforcement to take account of the management of health and safety and the development of safe systems of work as distinct from the avoidance of specific contraventions.

43 As a result, new procedures were introduced involving:

(a) mail shots to specific classifications of premises giving advice on appropriate health and safety literature;

(b) mail shots to specific classes of premises advising of the possibility of inspection in the near future;

(c) local central approaches;

(d) preliminary inspection of documentation, eg policy statements and, where appropriate, taking action on any deficiencies without actually inspecting the premises;

(e) in large complex premises, inspecting only selected areas with advice to the operator to extrapolate the deficiencies found to the entire premises.

44 Another authority, East Kilbride District Council, decided to carry out saturation inspection of specific work sectors such as butchers' shops, hairdressers, golf courses etc. The authority has identified certain advantages from using this approach, namely:

(a) it concentrates the mind of the inspector on the nature of the risks likely to be encountered and their relative importance;

(b) training of inspectors new to health and safety enforcement can be accelerated;

(c) combined with early follow up action, the approach has resulted in a high level of compliance in the premises concerned.

45 The City of Coventry obviously had quality assurance in mind when it developed an initiative involving sending out letters about office safety.

46 The letter informed the occupier of the new EC legislation and identified the key areas in the office that would be affected. It enclosed a self inspection questionnaire on health and safety issues. Finally, the letter asked for the recipients' comments on the content and presentation of the questionnaire, and offered assistance on any matter related to office health and safety.

USE OF NOTICES

47 Local authorities have increased their use of the formal improvement and prohibition notice procedure. The following examples illustrate the diversity of work activities covered and the degree to which notices can have an effect on health and safety standards.

48   One of the work activities which featured in the City of Glasgow District Council's enforcement strategy was cooling towers. Three improvement notices were issued on this subject. They included reference to the lack of routine maintenance, cleaning and disinfection, and to the absence of drift eliminators. Further information on this initiative is given in paragraphs 135-140.

49   An improvement notice was also issued restricting access to parts of a junior football ground in Glasgow when investigations revealed the presence of high levels of chromium waste in soil which formed part of the terracing. The contaminant was exposed and accessible to spectators.

50   A further notice was issued requiring the inspection of the windows/frames of a multi-storey hotel by a competent person following the fall of secondary glazing panels into the street below.

51   Unfortunately, some employers continue to fail to comply with their duties, even when notices have been issued. An inspector from one local authority visited a company which stored a variety of reclaimed materials including bricks, slates, stones, timber and metal products. He was concerned at the unsatisfactory state of the site, in particular the poor stacking of building materials and the imminent danger to which members of the public were unnecessarily exposed.

52   Improvement and prohibition notices were served on the company. The improvement notice listed works which were considered necessary to reduce the risk of collapse and the prohibition notice prohibited public access to the areas where building materials required restacking in accordance with the schedule attached to the improvement notice. Subsequent inspections by the Environmental Health Officer, who was accompanied by a Principal Specialist Inspector from HSE, revealed that neither notice had been complied with. Legal proceedings were instituted and following many arguments the defendant company finally pleaded guilty. Fines and costs totalling £2850 were imposed. The court also issued a court remedy order on the company.

LEGAL PROCEEDINGS

53   Kirklees Metropolitan Council was involved in two separate prosecutions both of which resulted in country-wide improvements on health and safety.

54   In the first, a member of the Environmental Health Department visited a national DIY/builders merchants on receipt of notification of an accident involving an employee who had been injured at a circular sawing machine. Investigation showed that the employee had not been properly trained and appropriate summonses were served. The company was fined £1000 with £222 costs. At the hearing they indicated that all of their employees had now received intensive training.

55   Again in response to an accident notification, an officer visited a retail store in the area. Investigation revealed that the store manager had broken his arm in five places after falling from an unguarded high level walkway in one of its storage areas. An improvement notice was served and legal proceedings were instituted. Fines and costs approaching £1000 were imposed. In mitigation the company's solicitor accepted that they were liable and said that steps had been taken in all 1100 branches throughout the country to ensure that a repetition of the accident did not occur.

56   The year covered by the report was one in which local authority inspectors began to consolidate their knowledge of the effects of recent legislation such as the Control of Substances Hazardous to Health Regulations (COSHH) and the Electricity at Work Regulations. They also learnt about the new problems to be faced in those sectors transferred to them in April 1990, particularly sport and leisure activities. This is reflected in the narrative sections of the annual returns (Forms LAE 1) received by LAU.

LEGISLATION   · · · · · · · · · · · ·

57   Many local authorities have reported that small employers, in particular, are still often unaware of the requirements imposed on them by the new legal requirements. This is despite the extensive advertising campaign by HSE for the COSHH legislation. Electrical installations in small food and catering establishments also attracted strong criticism. One district council in Scotland was so concerned about the lack of knowledge on COSHH that they carried out two special surveys on the subject, one being done in association with HSE and the other involving local hairdressers. Both surveys confirmed a high degree of ignorance on behalf of employers.

58   Some local authorities obviously feel they have now reached a point where enforcement is the only way forward as this extract from an LAE 1 demonstrates:

      "...this authority took its first prosecution under the COSHH Regulations. A shoe repair shop notified an incident involving an employee who was overcome by fumes whilst engaged in a new shoe dyeing process. The materials used contained solvents such as toluene and methyl ethyl ketone. An assessment of the risks created by the work had not been carried out. The employees were being required to work in an unventilated room, and exposure to the hazardous substances had not been prevented or adequately controlled."

      A fine of £1000 was imposed on the company.

59   The importance of meeting the requirements of the new Electricity at Work Regulations was clearly demonstrated by a report received concerning a fatal accident at a caravan park at a popular seaside resort. A young man went to use a shower and was electrocuted. The accident was investigated by the local authority enforcement officer with assistance from one of HSE's Principal Specialist Inspectors (Electrical Engineering). The cause was due to the electrical installation being in a poor condition and prohibition notices were served.

60   Although, as already indicated, general awareness of the Regulations was poor, one local authority found that its employers had a remarkably high awareness of the Electricity At Work Regulations. This was due to considerable commercial activity by local electrical contractors who were approaching businesses and offering testing services. Regrettably, some of the statements used by these contractors were inaccurate. Employers were being led to believe that tests must be carried out by members of particular bodies and that heavy fines would follow if employers did not sign up immediately. This resulted in the local authority receiving a number of enquiries from worried shop owners. There was also some suggestion that electricians did not make sufficient effort to explain that they were merely seeking business, leaving some confused employers with the impression that they had been approached by enforcement officers.

61 Two anecdotes from a Scottish authority indicate how far we have to go before acceptable standards are achieved.

"The power cable from a double knife sharpener had not been properly connected. The wires of the cable were wound round the pins of a plug connected to another cable which served the freezer. Thus one plug served two appliances." The only excuse given by the employer was that the sharpener had been acquired that day and they had not had time to purchase an additional plug.

"Similarly, during a routine inspection of a grocer's shop it was noted that an upturned two bar electric fire supported on one side by an old saucepan was being used as a cooking hot plate by staff. A frying pan containing cooking fat was found sitting on top of the upturned fire." The proprietor immediately removed the fire and replaced it with a microwave oven.

62 Another Scottish authority thought that the best way to improve standards of electrical safety at premises in their area was to start by training their own staff. A firm of consultants was engaged to give an in-house course on the Regulations. It gave both theoretical and hands on training in the subject. As a consequence, inspectors have been made more aware of simple electrical problems.

PREMISES

63 Local authorities appear to be putting a great deal of effort into inspecting those new premises allocated to them under the Health and Safety (Enforcing Authority) Regulations 1989. The following entry from one authority's annual return is typical of the work being done here.

"The transfer of private members and sports/leisure clubs by the enforcement regulations to the local authority has resulted in an inspection programme being undertaken. In the majority of cases this is the first health and safety inspection that the premises have received. It has been noted that the reaction has been encouraging in that most club managements have welcomed our involvement with interest. Many secretaries are familiar with the act, having come from an industrial background, but very few have considered the act in relation to their club activities.

The structure of most clubs was found to be in a safe condition and in good repair due, no doubt, to regular inspections by the fire and other authorities in connection with club registration. The absence of any formalised health and safety management was, however, almost universally found.

Enforcement has been concentrated in this area. The considerable resources dedicated to advising the management of these clubs has been productive, with the formulation of safety policies, COSHH assessments and, in some cases, the establishment of a safety audit procedure. There has not, as yet, been any need to resort to formal enforcement procedures."

64 Some of the premises transferred have presented local authorities with difficult and complex enforcement issues. Motor sports are typical. This includes everything from Formula 1 racing where very stringent in-house controls exist, to ad hoc venues where there is little or no control. Diving activities are also a matter for concern, as the following case from early 1991 illustrates. It did not appear in the 1990/91 report as legal proceedings were instigated and the complexity of the case meant that it was not completed until 1991/92.

A 40-year-old man drowned while undergoing training at a sub aqua club diving school.

The deceased had undergone both theoretical and practical training in sub-aqua diving by attending courses at his local training college and in the local school swimming pool. He then progressed to attending a training session run by a diving school at a disused clay pit.

He was one of three divers under the supervision of a diving instructor and dive master. The five divers, led by the instructor, swam in Indian file to a platform at 5 m depth. Before they could progress any further the deceased person indicated to the instructor that he was out of air. Despite attempts by the instructor and the dive master to re-establish an air supply from their own spare regulators and carry out a rescue, the deceased sank to the bottom of the clay pit and drowned. On examination, his air cylinder was found to be empty.

The diving instructor had failed to obtain an HSE part IV restricted certificate entitling him to instruct amateur divers in the course of employment. He was subsequently prosecuted for this and other offences under the Diving Operations at Work Regulations. A fine of £400 was imposed along with costs of £125.25. Improvement notices and a prohibition notice were also served on the proprietor of the diving school.

The importance of training being undertaken by authorised and experienced instructors, proper maintenance of equipment used by divers, and the provision of adequate reserve air supplies for novice divers are essential in ensuring that similar incidents of this type do not occur in the future.

Special working groups

RETAIL VIOLENCE

65   Concern about the problem of violence in the workplace continues to grow and the need for sector specific guidance resulted in this group being set up. Membership consists of the British Retail Consortium (BRC), relevant trade unions, local authorities, independent experts and HSE. A review of available guidance for this sector has been carried out and a number of BRC members have provided data on incidents which they have recorded. A common recording system would be required for comparisons to be made but the group consider that practical advice based on best practice is a realistic aim for the sector.

66   A separate working group has looked at the need for guidance in the financial services sector. The group, chaired by HSE's General Policy Branch, produced a consultative document on the draft guidance in January 1993 and hopes to publish the final guidance later in the year.

SHOPPING TROLLEYS

Guidance

67   The local authorities' report for 1990/91 gave background information on the development of safety guidance and a draft British Standard on the construction and design of shopping trolleys.

68   Guidance on shopping trolley safety, *Shopping trolleys safe system of work guidance* [1] was published in September 1992.

69   Proposals for a European Standard on the construction and design of shopping trolleys overtook the

work which was being co-ordinated by the Local Authority Unit on behalf of HELA. Nevertheless, as a result of the activities of the HELA working group, HSE commissioned research from its Research and Laboratory Services Division (RLSD) into the fundamental question of shopping trolley stability. The results of this work have been incorporated in British proposals for a European Standard.

Stability research

70   Early in 1991, the Research and Laboratory Services Division of the Health and Safety Executive (RLSD) was asked to examine several shopping trolleys from shops where children had been injured while riding in the seats of the trolleys. As a result of this work RLSD was asked to assist in formulating a suitable test to assess the stability of trolleys.

Incident investigations

71   Although there is no British Standard governing the design of shopping trolleys, suppliers to the UK market (British, French and German) have been using stability test criteria contained in French AFNOR and German DIN Standards. Trolleys examined following incidents were generally found to conform to those standards. However, RLSD was concerned that the tests, which used a static weight on the seat to 'simulate' a child, did not properly cover the range of positions a child could adopt. RLSD therefore decided to assess the stability of the trolleys using a 15 kg anthropometric child dummy.

72   While sitting in the seats of trolleys, children are likely to adopt any position which the constraints of the trolley will allow. The stability of the trolleys was therefore assessed with this in mind. The results showed that trolleys were significantly less stable with a child dummy leaning in the seat than with either an upright child dummy or a test weight placed on the seat.

A new British Standard test

73   As a result of the above work it was considered that existing test criteria were inadequate and RLSD was therefore asked to devise a new test. It was thought to be impractical to devise a method which uses child dummies because of cost.

74   In order to get a representative sample of the variation in trolley designs, both in detail design and size, several trolleys were obtained from each of four principal manufacturers. A computer modelling technique was used to help in designing a new British Standard test. The design of the computer model was refined until the original 1991 tests of the incident trolleys were simulated with sufficient accuracy to be able to use the computer method with confidence for other designs of trolley.

The recommended test method

75   Although a more complex test was contemplated, the computer model demonstrated that a change to the test slope angle of the existing test method would take account of a leaning child in the trolley seat. Manufacturers have expressed an interest in the computer model as it will enable them to place the dummy in a facsimile of new trolley designs before the prototype stage. This would allow the trolley design to be optimised for maximum stability while still accommodating other design constraints to suit customer requirements.

76   The information contained in Part 3 of this annual report is supplied by local authorities on a voluntary basis from two sources. Firstly, local authorities provide the LAU with copies of the RIDDOR accident report form (Form F2508) sent to them by employers; secondly they complete a voluntary annual statistical return (LAE 1) which contains detailed information on numbers of premises, enforcement action and staff resources in their areas.

77   During 1991/92, HELA agreed to the creation of a special working group to review the LAE 1 form. This working group was made up of experienced local authority inspectors supported by the Local Authority Unit and HSE's Statistical Services Unit.

78   The working group met during the summer of 1991 and its report was endorsed by HELA in November 1991. New forms will be introduced with effect from the 1993/4 reporting year. Local authorities have already been made aware of the new forms and the main computer software houses who supply management information systems to local authority environmental health and trading standards services are fully aware of these changes.

79   The main changes proposed by the review will improve the efficiency and effectiveness of data collection. They include:

(a)   simplifying the return to a single form for the whole of Great Britain (previously separate forms were sent to local authorities in England and Wales, and in Scotland);

(b)   information requested from LAs on visits by inspectors has been simplified, and brought into line with common practice;

(c)   information on enforcement action has been extended to enable the consequences of action on different sectors to be identified.

80   In addition, the review proposed that a few questions should be capable of change from year to year. This allows HELA to target particular issues on a one-off basis. For 1993/94, it has selected training and the impact of the European Directives as its major topics. For the future, HELA will review these issues annually to assess possible targets for enquiry.

81   The review also proposed that a second form (LAE 2) should be created to capture information on the enforcement of those other relevant statutory provisions carried out by English Metropolitan Authorities, and Counties, London Boroughs, and Scottish Regions. Its main focus will be activities such as Petroleum Licensing, Explosives and Firework Acts enforcement. The LAE 2 will follow the structure of the revised LAE 1 and include questions on visits, resources and enforcement action. As with the LAE 1, there is a targeted question regarding the enforcement of the new European Directives. There are also particular questions for 1993/94 on the operation of the Explosives Act.

82   One change recommended by the working group and already implemented by HELA since the 1990/91 report has been to ensure that those local authorities who complete and return their LAE 1 form are acknowledged. This is done in the form of an appendix to the reports.

83   The working group also discussed the possibility of creating a national prosecutions database, similar to the accident database already held by the LAU. This issue requires careful consideration and has been remitted for further consideration to the enforcement policy working group, which will report to HELA during 1993/94.

CATERING SAFETY

84 In early 1992 the Local Authority Unit was approached by the leader of HSE's Food National Interest Group, which acts as the centre of expertise on health and safety in the food industry. He was concerned about accident rates in the catering industry, which are high when compared with other manufacturing sectors, and wanted to establish a Catering Committee. This would have the aim of providing a forum for all interested parties to discuss health and safety issues in the catering industry and, where possible, provide advice and guidance to employers and employees. Because of the overlap of enforcement of health and safety in catering it was seen as essential that LAs had close involvement with the committee.

85 The committee first met in the spring of 1992 when its aims and objectives were established. A smaller working group, jointly led by LAU and the Food NIG, was founded to carry forward the initial work on raising the profile of health and safety in the catering sector and, in particular, flagging up the importance of the new EC led legislation. This work is now well in hand.

MANUAL HANDLING

86 In addition to the special working groups established through the HELA system, other ad hoc working parties are formed as and when necessary. The Local Authority Unit has an involvement in many of these, a typical example being that on safe practices for the manual handling of drinks during delivery. This working group is led by a representative from HSE's Drinks NIG, and includes members from the relevant employers and trade union organisations.

87 The guidance produced by HSE on the new Manual Handling Regulations encourages industries to produce their own codes of practice to help in the provision of clear guidance to employers on the standards to be achieved in order to meet the legal requirements. Such guidance would be of particular benefit to the drinks industry because manual handling is the major cause of its accidents.

88 The work of the committee is now almost complete and publication of the guidance document is expected to take place in mid-1993.

Published guidance

RETAIL AND WHOLESALE WAREHOUSES

89 Alan Air, a Senior Environmental Health Officer from Gateshead Metropolitan District Council carried forward the work on guidance for this sector. A guidance booklet[2] was published on 1 December 1992 and launched at the Dynamic Warehouse Exhibition at Stoneleigh, Warwickshire with help from Warwick District Council and the Institution of Environmental Health Officers.

GOLF COURSE HEALTH AND SAFETY

90 Work started on this project in 1991 and was initially carried out by James MacIntyre, a Principal Agricultural Inspector who has since retired from HSE. There is considerable interest in this topic and the sector appears eager to obtain a comprehensive document. Areas to be covered include the safe use of pesticides and agricultural type machinery. Publication is expected during 1993.

. . . .

RESIDENTIAL CARE HOMES AND HORSE-RIDING ESTABLISHMENTS

91   Work on these projects began in February 1992 when Judy Lyons, an Environmental Health Officer from Doncaster Metropolitan District Council joined the LAU on secondment. The research and drafting of the residential care homes guidance has been completed and the draft sent for external consultation. Publication is planned for the summer of 1993.

92   Judy Lyons brought with her a detailed knowledge of horse riding and has also managed to produce a draft document on health and safety in horse-riding establishments. This item was on the list of guidance projects and is also expected to be published during 1993.

The enforcement liaison officer system

93   Enforcement liaison officers (ELOs) are HSE principal inspectors, based in each of HSE's 20 area offices. They form an essential part of a network providing technical and legal advice and support to local authorities. During the year some 900 days were spent providing this support and marshalling other HSE resources such as specialist inspectors and scientists working in regionally based Field Consultant Groups and doctors and nurses from the Employment Medical Advisory Service (EMAS) where appropriate.

94   The system is managed by a unit within HSE's Field Operations Division (FOD) headquarters which also provides the link with LAU. Annual plans of work are agreed with ELOs and statistical and narrative returns received at the end of the work planning year. In June 1992 a report on the work of the ELOs was presented to HELA for the first time and this is to be the pattern for future years.

95   ELOs attend an annual residential conference which gives the ELOs, LAU, and FOD the opportunity to come together as a group. The joint chairmen of HELA and senior representatives of FOD also attend. The conference provides more than just a forum for discussion: it aims to enhance the effectiveness of the ELO system. Debate is usually lively and constructive. At the most recent conference 14 clearly defined action points were taken away to be pursued. With so many different players in the system, the need for better communications is always at the forefront of the debate.

. . . .

JOINT INITIATIVES

96   In recent years a number of HGV drivers in London have been killed or seriously injured while coupling their articulated lorry tractor units to parked trailers in factory, warehouse and large retail outlet trailer parks. The accidents often occur as a result of trailer handbrakes not being applied when parking. When the tractor unit is connected, the trailer's road brakes are deactivated. If the handbrake has not been applied the whole unit can free-wheel away, crushing the driver.

97   Concern about the frequency of these accidents led to a joint LA/HSE cross London inspection and enforcement initiative on lorry trailer park safety. The initiative was planned and led by EHOs from

three London boroughs and involved 286 visits to 128 trailer parks by 75 inspectors from 24 local authorities and two HSE areas. A special leaflet was produced for this initiative.

98   Over a third of the trailers examined were found not to have the handbrake applied and enforcement action was taken in 39 premises. Half the premises visited were found to have other trailer park deficiencies such as poor layout or no lighting.

99   During 1990 a small firms initiative took place in West Yorkshire, and in 1991 Calderdale, Kirklees and Wakefield Metropolitan Districts agreed to take part in a repeat exercise. HSE was concerned about safety in small firms and wanted to put particular emphasis on inspection of these premises.

100   The initiative involved inspection of small firms in Calderdale, Kirklees and Wakefield by a team of 20 inspectors from HSE, and 30 from the local authorities. The theme for the week was training, and the exercise utilised the resources of the Training and Enterprise Councils, including exhibitions at the two local TECs. Eric Forth, Minister of State at the Department of Employment, attended the exhibition at the Calderdale and Kirklees TEC.

101   The local authorities visited 235 premises in the area over a 2 day period. Fifty-eight improvement and four prohibition notices were issued, and legal proceedings were considered appropriate in one case.

SECONDMENT

102   Last year's report made reference to an HSE inspector seconded to an LA as a principal EHO. A unique opportunity arose for a 9 month secondment to a metropolitan borough council of a main grade factory inspector acting as a principal officer heading up an Occupational Health and Safety Section consisting of two EHOs and one technical assistant.

103   The overall purpose of the job was to manage the occupational health team by pursuing priorities in order to maintain and improve standards of compliance in accordance with legislative requirements, Codes of Practice, and the policy of the authority. An early need for the introduction of a planned strategy covering both inspection and enforcement was identified. It was clear that the section faced similar difficulties to those of a typical HSE industry group and it was decided to introduce some of the techniques which had proved useful to HSE.

104   The main objectives were considered to be:

(a) Raising health and safety standards in LA enforced premises and raising the enforcement profile by selective and formal action.

(b) Introducing effective priority planning and work recording systems.

(c) Training - providing a guide on legal practices and meeting the individual needs of staff by a range of solutions including: attendance on HSE or IEHO courses; introducing open learning; and carrying out joint visiting as part of the learning process.

(d) Raising general awareness of health and safety including requirements on accident reporting (RIDDOR).

(e) Identifying the risks in premises newly allocated to the local authority under the 1989 Regulations by sample inspection.

(f) Co-ordinating the work on safety in sports grounds.

105 A planned work programme was produced for the following year with specific objectives for inspection based on a priority rating scheme together with work on selected special projects. The special inspection projects ranged widely, including: animal care premises and riding establishments; kennels and catteries; tyre and exhaust fitting centres; sports clubs and golf courses; churches and chapels by sample; follow up work on residential homes; fork-lift truck training; fast food premises; and consideration of the forthcoming Regulations on display screen equipment and manual handling.

106 The secondment was of benefit to the individual concerned, the local authority and to HSE. The seconded inspector gained management experience; exposure to a diverse range of issues, many of which were outside his previous experience; and knowledge of the internal workings of local authorities including the characteristics of local politics and the committee structure. The local authority benefited through the introduction of some improved systems and procedures, training, and improved awareness of the HSE resources available through the ELO system. HSE gained an enhanced awareness of local authority systems and procedures which will inform policy making.

107 The inspector concluded that, in general, the combined objectives were realised and recommended that this secondment could be seen as a starting point for further attachment of HSE inspectors to local authorities. This would contribute to the enhancement of consistent health and safety enforcement.

Training

TRAINING IN THE LOCAL AUTHORITY SECTOR

108 Many local authorities have been heavily involved in training, both in respect of their own staff and in the provision of training for employers and employees in the sectors for which they have enforcement responsibilities. The latter helps to create a better understanding and degree of co-operation between employers and local authority inspectors.

109 During 1990/91 a seminar was hosted by the Environmental Health Department in Glasgow for an invited audience of companies which undertake window cleaning. The seminar was very successful and has been followed up in 1991/92 with two further information sessions. The first of these was for the operators of entertainment premises, highlighting the potential hazards associated with overcrowding and other matters specifically relevant to discotheques and similar premises. The second information session covered similar topics, although the audience in this case were the major brewers and hoteliers, who are considered to have widespread influence in the city in respect of the management of health and safety.

110 The sessions were used to emphasise the management of safety, the need for self regulation, and the importance of staff training in health and safety matters. Comment was also made on passive smoking, and the new Regulations to be introduced from 1 January 1993.

111 Portsmouth Environmental Health Department decided to put effort into promoting training validated by the Institution of Environmental Health Officers. As a result, a total of 11 basic health and safety courses were run, involving 149 candidates.

112 Gateshead Metropolitan Borough Council worked with HSE to increase the awareness of employers and employees on health and safety matters generally and training in particular. An information pack was prepared and handed out to as many companies as possible over a 2 day inspection period involving 8 EHOs and 15 HSE inspectors. Eighty-one premises were inspected by EHOs, 12 enforcement notices issued, and follow up visits made. The local press and radio stations provided excellent coverage of the exercise.

113   On a final note, we should not forget the important contribution that County Liaison Groups can make to training. Thirty-two groups operate at local level to provide a useful forum for consideration of common problems, exchanging information and enabling consistency of enforcement at a local level. Items of national interest are fed into the HELA system where appropriate. Many of the groups act as a training forum by facilitating specialised training of enforcement officers within the Counties.

HSE ISSUES

114   The Health and Safety Commission's policy statement on health and safety training was published in its plan of work for 1991/92. It provided the framework for a wide variety of HSE activities to improve the quality and quantity of health and safety training.

115   HSE has forged links with Lead Bodies who are developing standards of competence which will eventually lead to National Vocational Qualifications and Scottish Vocational Qualifications. HSE's aim has been to ensure that the standards adequately cover health and safety. The Local Authority Unit has similarly been in contact with Lead Bodies developing standards of competence for occupations enforced by local authorities. HSE has assisted in a research project which will help the National Council for Vocational Qualification and SCOTVEC (the Scottish Vocational Education Council) in the revision of the guidance for Lead Bodies.

116   HSE is providing the secretariat to the Occupational Health and Safety Lead Body, which is developing standards of competence relevant to health and safety practitioners, eg safety advisers, hygienists and enforcement officers (from both local authorities and HSE). The Lead Body is now chaired by Mr Rex Symons, a Health and Safety Commission member. The work will be continuing well into 1993.

117   There has been extensive contact between HSE's Field Operations Division and local Training and Enterprise Councils (TECs) as one part of a wider campaign to target small firms. A joint initiative which took place in West Yorkshire, involving HSE, local authorities and TECs, is described in paragraphs 99-101 of this report.

118   For the first time HSC has sponsored a special award for health and safety training under the Employment Department's 1992 National Training Awards competition. This was as a contribution to the European Year of Safety, Hygiene and Health Protection at Work.

The lead authority pilot trails

119   Local authorities have recognised that, with many large companies operating in a number of areas, there is likely to be some duplication of their effort in inspecting premises and evaluating systems separately. In addition, there has been a trend by increasingly sophisticated national companies to standardise health and safety management systems across their outlets, which may operate in many

local authority areas. A lead authority approach, whereby one LA reviews health and safety management systems according to a standard model, could prove to be a more effective and efficient way of dealing with these situations.

120   A health and safety lead authority is a local authority, selected by HELA, with the main health and safety decision-making base of a company located in its area. Its function is to act as a focus for LA relations with that company.

121   The June 1992 meeting of HELA endorsed proposals to carry out five pilot trials during 1992/93 to test how the lead authority principle works in practice.

122   Five LAs and companies were selected by HELA for the pilot trials. These are:

Dundee and Wm Low;

Kirklees and Consultant Cleaning Services;

Birmingham and Ansells (Retail)Ltd;

South Bedfordshire and Granada Hospitality and;

Harrow and Wickes Building Supplies.

123   These companies include food retailing services, peripatetic service providers, public houses, entertainment and DIY/Building supplies retailing; and they vary in size from companies with less than 100 outlets to two with more than 500.

124   Each lead authority will initially carry out a safety management review of its company, based upon the principles set out in *Successful Health and Safety Management* [3]. A safety management review is an evaluation of a company's health and safety management system, and what has been done to assess and reduce the risks in its business. It involves the lead authority in discussions with key employees and, where possible, verification of the company's systems.

125   The safety management review will enable the lead authority to understand how the company works and to take a far more strategic view of that company's operations than might be possible from a general inspection of a single outlet.

126   Following the review, a report will be submitted to the company for its consideration. Details of the report and the company response will be made available to enforcing authorities who have an outlet in their area. This will help inform LAs about the companies' health and safety management systems.

127   After successful completion of the review, the lead authority will act as a source of expertise on that company and a point of contact for other LAs.

128   The other main function of the lead authority will be to collate and filter the enquiries it receives. In this way, issues which have a significance for other companies in the same sector, industry or even nationally, can be more easily identified and passed on through the HELA network to all enforcing authorities.

129   Responsibility for enforcement action by a local authority will remain unchanged. The lead authority approach is not intended to fetter the discretion of any enforcing authority.

130   Training in the techniques of a safety management review took place in November 1992 and lead authorities were able to start work with their companies before the end of the year. It is expected that LAs will have produced their reports in the early spring of 1993, and will then begin to provide help and support to other enforcing authorities with company outlets in their area. HELA has asked for an evaluation report to be prepared for its meeting in early 1994.

Occupational health

131 Data from the HSE supplement on health and safety to the 1990 Labour Force Survey suggest that, in the UK alone, around three-quarters of a million workers took time off work in 1989/90 because of work-related illness.

132 In September 1992 HELA presented a paper to the Health and Safety Commission proposing an occupational health policy for local authorities as enforcers of health and safety legislation. The paper was approved by the Commission and local authorities were informed of the outcome.

133 The HELA policy tackles the issue of occupational health through five key elements: identification and prioritisation; information; prevention; enforcement; and review. This is consistent with HSE's approach to the issue, and LAU are now drawing up a work plan to implement the policy. Work on the first element has already begun.

134 This approach of identifying a priority area of concern and moving towards formal enforcement via a programme of information gathering and prevention by inspection, advice, guidance and publicity is not entirely new. Some local authorities have already successfully used it to address areas of particular concern. For example, the City of Glasgow District Council when considering the risks associated with wet cooling towers.

LEGIONELLOSIS AND COOLING TOWER INSTALLATIONS IN GLASGOW

135 Following a major community acquired outbreak of Legionnaire's disease in Glasgow in the 1980s, it became clear that action was required to ensure that the operators of cooling towers were aware of published guidance on their safe operation and that the guidelines were being followed.

136 An exploratory survey was conducted in 1988 by the Environmental Health Department and the Department of Community Medicine at Glasgow University. The survey sought to confirm the exact number of towers and measure the degree of compliance with recommended operating procedures by their users. The results showed that most towers were moderately well maintained, but that there were sufficient shortcomings to warrant a programme of action.

137 In each year since 1988 all of the towers which are the responsibility of the Environmental Health Department for enforcement purposes have been inspected. In 1991 there were 98 buildings containing 223 cooling towers in the city. Of these, 31 buildings and the 62 towers they contained were the responsibility of the Environmental Health Department.

138 The Department's strategy has been to introduce enforcement progressively. In the early stages the objective was to offer advice and guidance where shortcomings were identified by inspection, with advisory letters being sent to operators of unsatisfactory towers in 1989. By 1991/92 action had been stepped up to the serving of formal Improvement Notices under the terms of the Health and Safety at Work etc Act 1974. As a part of this strategy the department has taken action to ensure that all operators are aware of new developments. For example, when the Approved Code of Practice on *The prevention or control of legionellosis (including Legionnaire's disease)* [4], with accompanying HSE booklet [5], came into effect on 15 January 1992 and confirmed many of the issues already raised with operators in Glasgow, the Department wrote to all operators. The letter advised them of the introduction of the Code of Practice and said that inspectors would take account of the Code's practical guidance during their enforcement activities.

139   The programme of inspection and advice has proved to be a success, having brought about significant improvements in the design of tower installations and in working practices. For example, in 1989 23% of the towers did not have drift eliminators. By 1990 this had been reduced to 7%, with the operators concerned proposing to install eliminators. Over the same period, the proportion of premises without a "nominated person" responsible for tower maintenance fell from 41% to 17%. Between 1990 and 1991the proportion of premises which protected staff by chlorinating towers prior to draining and cleaning rose dramatically from 24% to 100%.

140   By 1991 the standard of maintenance, treatment and control of cooling towers in the city was generally good, with many operators fulfilling much more than their basic obligations. Formal enforcement action was only necessary in three cases, where Improvement Notices were issued. As a result the operators concerned took action to comply with the Environmental Health Department's requirements.

The Notification of Cooling Towers and Evaporative Condensers Regulations 1992

141   The 1990/91 Report on Health and Safety in the Service Industries referred to HELA's involvement in the consultation leading to the drafting of regulations on cooling tower registration. New Regulations requiring the notification of all premises containing wet cooling towers or evaporative condensers came into force on 2 November 1992. The requirement will provide investigators with valuable information on the location of this type of equipment in the event of an outbreak of disease. Notification must be made to the local authority in which the premises are situated, on a form approved by HSE. The form was drawn up in consultation with HELA, and has been kept as simple as possible in order to minimise administrative burdens on employers and local authorities.

'LIGHTEN THE LOAD'

142   In September 1991 HSE launched a major campaign called 'Lighten the Load'. It aims to raise the awareness of and promote the prevention of musculoskeletal disorders caused or made worse by work. As these are of concern in the local authority enforced sector, LAs are taking part in the campaign. It is operating in three phases over a 3-year period. Phase 1 concentrated on work related upper limb disorders. Phase 2 will focus on disorders from manual handling operations and will run throughout 1993. It will take account of the new manual handling Regulations which came into force early in 1993. Other musculoskeletal disorders will not be ignored - the impact of new Regulations concerning the use of display screen equipment will also be taken into consideration. The final phase in 1994 will focus on ergonomics, particularly the benefits of good ergonomics in the workplace.

143   To promote and prepare for Lighten the Load, the Employment Medical Advisory Service, which is spearheading the campaign, has been much involved in providing training. This aims to enable non-occupational health specialists to identify cases or risk factors for work related musculoskeletal disorders, and advise on ways to eradicate or minimise these. Training was extended to LA inspectors, who have attended study days and workshops either run specially for them or as part of a general audience. During Phase 1 at least 15 lectures/seminars were given specifically for local

authority enforcement officers by EMAS with 600 individual officers attending. Similar levels of training and support will be offered to officers for Phases 2 and 3 of the campaign. This will be planned and initiated on an area basis by EMAS teams.

144 As well as taking the campaign forward themselves, local authority enforcement officers have also used EMAS occupational health expertise on joint visits to investigate some cases of musculoskeletal disorders. EMAS and the enforcement officers work together to investigate, advise and enforce as appropriate. For example, many retail outlets take delivery of goods which are heavy or awkward to handle. In one shop, problems were occurring because clothes were delivered in boxes and had to be manually transferred onto hangers. In another, lifting and loading barrels and crates in a restricted space was identified as an unsafe system of work. Thanks to intervention by the enforcement officer and with the assistance of EMAS, this kind of problem can be tackled. The kind of help given may include advising a company how to introduce written safe systems of work, the provision of training in lifting techniques, and advising on the setting up of monitoring procedures to identify any new or recurring health problems. In the long term, Lighten the Load should help reduce both the number of people suffering from musculoskeletal disorders and the cost to industry this causes.

MUSCULOSKELETAL DISORDERS IN SUPERMARKET CASHIERS

145 In the past it was suggested that the operation of some supermarket check-outs was associated with high levels of musculoskeletal disorders, principally affecting the lower back, upper arm-shoulder-neck and wrist-hand. Scant information has been available about the extent of these problems or their severity, the variety of ways in which they may manifest themselves and how they may vary from store to store and from company to company. As this issue is likely to be of concern to LA inspectors, the Local Authority Unit worked as part of an HSE inter-divisional working group which sponsored a 1 day workshop at Surrey University. This led to a study by HSE's Research and Laboratory Services and Technology and Health Sciences Divisions to measure the prevalence of musculoskeletal pain among supermarket cashiers and to examine any relationships between this and particular working practices. The aim was to highlight what could be improved (from a health and safety perspective) in check-out work and check-out equipment.

146 Cashiers were asked about their perceived health and the acceptability of check-out work and their working environment by using self-administered questionnaires. These data were compared to an ergonomist's assessment of the workplace, and an analysis of movements and postures, which were recorded on video while the cashier processed the customers provisions. Data were collected for 1830 cashiers from 47 supermarkets operating 11 different check-out systems. Work is also planned using direct measurement of muscular activity and analysis of posture to assess the loading on various muscle groups. This work will enable design features of checkouts to be evaluated.

147 Analysis of the data is continuing. Initial results suggest the prevalence for disorders of the neck, elbow and wrist-hands cannot be attributed to any one particular check-out system and were found to be of small magnitude compared to the results found in other working populations. The prevalence of disorders of the shoulders, upper and lower back, knees and feet-ankles however, varied significantly according to the type of check-out operated. Efforts to explain this are continuing but provisional thoughts point to a number of factors. Foot-ankle and knee disorders were more likely at check-out systems which were

operated while standing. Where cashiers were seated, both they and the ergonomists noted a number of common problems with the seats provided. These included: a need for repair or maintenance, especially of adjustment mechanisms; poor quality seat padding; or inappropriate design and selection for check-out work. Many seats would not adjust sufficiently high to enable the cashier to hold the provisions in a comfortable manner. Other examples of poor check-out design included scales being positioned far above shoulder height and seated cashiers having to lean to the left to undertake the main check-out activities. Complaints of numbness in the left leg and discomfort in the back were sometimes reported. This was thought to be due to the postures adopted and the failure or inability to use the seat back-rest. The need for a foot-rest was highlighted by damage to shelving within the check-out desk caused by cashiers putting their feet on it or the use of up-turned hand baskets. At a time when retailers are looking at their product range in the light of the new Regulations on manual handling, the cashiers wrote particularly about difficulties with handling heavy and bulky products such as bags of dog food, cat litter, multi-packs of drinks, potatoes and washing powder.

148   A fuller report aimed at retailers and designers of check-out equipment is under preparation, along with an assessment system for local authority inspectors. It is anticipated that recommendations will focus on the positioning of some check-out features, seating, appropriate design to avoid poor working postures and movements, and work organisation.

PASSIVE SMOKING AT WORK

149   The health effects of breathing other people's tobacco smoke (passive smoking) at work continues to be an issue raised with local authority inspectors by employees in offices and other enclosed workplaces.

150   The publication of the Fourth Report of the Independent Scientific Committee on Smoking and Health in 1988 gave inspectors a basis upon which to encourage employers to formulate, adopt and monitor policies on smoking. Many local authorities also raised the awareness of passive smoking as a public health issue by conducting educational campaigns and support, especially on the designated "no-smoking day".

151   In September 1992, HSE published a revision of its earlier booklet on passive smoking at work, published in 1988. The new advisory booklet urges all employers to develop and implement, in consultation with their employees or their representatives, a policy on smoking. Non-smoking should be regarded as the norm in enclosed workplaces and priority should be given to non-smokers with special provision for smokers. The booklet sets out ways to achieve a smoke-free environment at the workplace.

152   The new booklet also describes the health risks, lists the advantages to employers of voluntarily introducing a policy on smoking and explains how this should result in better employee health, greater efficiency, improved industrial relations and financial benefits.

153   The booklet contains information on legal duties including the new Workplace (Health, Safety and Welfare) Regulations which require non-smoking workers to be protected from discomfort caused by tobacco smoke in rest rooms or rest areas. Local authority inspectors will be able to use this booklet to advise employers on smoking policies to fit the individual circumstances at the particular workplace.

General

154 The European Year of Health and Safety commenced towards the end of this report period on 1 March 1992. Local authorities were active in initial preparations for it, with many of them attending the seven launch events on 17 March 1992 and signing up to support the year.

155 Many authorities applied for the limited funding available from the EC for projects in support of the Year. Ten of the 26 UK projects recommended for funding in the first round (starting in the period March to September 1992) were run by local authorities.

156 At a press conference to introduce the Year, in January 1992, Mr Eric Forth, Parliamentary Under Secretary of State for Employment, presented cheques to two successful applicants, including the Royal Environmental Health Institute of Scotland (REHIS), who fitted out a health and safety bus to travel throughout Scotland giving advice and information to people at work.

157 Another early participant in the Year's activities was Calderdale Metropolitan Borough Council, which, together with the councils of Bradford, Leeds, Kirklees, and Wakefield, organised a health and safety roadshow. Bradford Metropolitan Borough Council also organised a 2 day exhibition in March with practical activities linked to the new manual handling legislation.

158 A seminar organized by Leicester City Council in March, provided an opportunity for the participants to benefit from the presence of enforcement officers from HSE, the Council's Environmental Department, and specialist business advisers. Among the subjects covered were the new health and safety Regulations, workplace injuries and the health and safety responsibilities of employers.

159 Other authorities developing projects for the Year included Sheffield City Council, who planned to use the historical and artistic records in their museums and galleries to stimulate interest and awareness in health and safety issues among young people at schools and colleges. Seven West Midlands authorities - Wolverhampton, Walsall, Birmingham, Dudley, Sandwell, Coventry and Solihull - also set up a touring caravan to visit small firms, town centres and industrial estates, to heighten general awareness of good and safe practices.

THE REPORTING OF INJURIES, DISEASES AND DANGEROUS OCCURRENCES REGULATIONS 1985 (RIDDOR)

160 During the year the Health and Safety Commission received a report on a review of the first 5 years of operation of the Reporting of Injuries, Diseases and Dangerous Occurrences Regulations 1985. The local authorities contributed to the review, which also took account of the findings of a trailer to the 1990 Labour Force Survey, on occupational injuries and ill health.

161 The review indicated that as many as 70% of reportable injuries are not notified to the enforcing authorities. It showed that while many employers are unaware of the Regulations, many more are confused by the different categories of injury and different reporting requirements.

162 The recommendation that the Regulations be amended to simplify both the reporting requirements and the reporting arrangements has been accepted by HSC. A consultative document detailing proposed changes will be published in due course.

163 However, despite the above, local authorities were still doing their best to ensure compliance with RIDDOR throughout the year 1991/92. For example, the Lincolnshire Health and Safety Liaison Committee, which consists of representative inspectors from each of the Lincolnshire authorities, looked particularly at accidents at work. They decided to initiate a county-wide campaign involving media coverage, posters etc.

164 In East Lindsey, one of the Lincolnshire districts, the reported accident figures for 1991/92 have shown a fall over the previous year of approximately 26%. Although the number of firms submitting accident reports does not appear to have altered significantly, one local company which gave rise to the major component of the accident figures has, following a number of safety initiatives encouraged by local authority inspectors, reduced the number of accidents of all kinds by 39%. However, the authority anticipates that accident figures for next year will increase, due to the Lincolnshire campaign to encourage reporting described above. The increase will be made more acute by the authority's recent insistence on the formalising of accident reporting procedures from a motor racing circuit in the area.

165 Other local authorities have similar problems. In one, the establishment of a large supermarket has brought about a notable increase in accidents, as has the transfer under the Enforcing Authority Regulations of a motor sport activity.

166 South Ribble Borough Council decided to liaise closely with local fire authorities over fire incidents to ensure that, where applicable, these were notified under RIDDOR as dangerous occurrences. Once again, this is likely to lead to a significant increase in the accident figures.

167 Members of the East and West Sussex Health and Safety Liaison Group produced a poster to advise all those in the workplace of the need to report accidents. The poster has been widely distributed to

workplaces; doctors' surgeries; the accident and emergency units of district general hospitals etc. It is too early to determine whether or not the poster campaign has produced the desired effect. However, the poster and the message it conveys have been generally well received.

CENTRAL APPROACH AUDITS

168 Two companies of contrasting size and organisation were the subject of central approach audits carried out during 1991/92 by Andrew Foster, an Environmental Health Team Leader from the London Borough of Hackney, while seconded to HSE's Accident Prevention Advisory Unit (APAU).

169 One of these companies was a regional chain of retail shops which had been prosecuted following a fatal accident in which an employee had fallen from a fork lift truck. The audit showed that although senior managers had recognised the need to improve the company's health and safety performance, and were producing a new health and safety procedures manual, they needed a formalised written plan setting objectives for improving health and safety, against which they could judge their progress. Some of their procedures for controlling risks needed improving, including those for fork lift truck safety, and some high risk activities had no health and safety procedure.

170 HSE's Research and Laboratory Services Division has recently investigated the reasons why lift trucks overturn. The project, commissioned by HSE's Safety Policy and Technology Divisions, has resulted in the production of a video *Dangerous Manoeuvres* [6], which shows the main causes of lift truck overturns. In addition, the HSE guidance booklet *Safety in working with lift trucks* [7] has been revised.

171 The other central approach audit involved a major company in the catering sector, and similarly it had no written health and safety plan formally agreed by its senior managers. In both companies the role and responsibility of all line managers for ensuring the health and safety of those working in their work area, or area of control, were not clearly expressed or understood.

172 Other work by Andrew Foster involved developing the methodology for safety management reviews which are being carried out by lead authorities as part of the Lead Authority Pilot Project, and providing advice and assistance during their conduct. See paragraphs 119-130.

Relevant statutory provisions

173 The responsibilities of trading standards officers (TSOs) in enforcing certain relevant statutory provisions under the Health and Safety at Work etc Act (HSWA) are set out in paragraph 2 of Appendix Five. In addition to these activities, overlapping principles in legislation can mean that health and safety becomes an important factor when carrying out their other duties; for example, when enforcing consumer protection legislation.

GAS SAFETY IN CARAVANS

174 In 1991 four people died in two separate incidents as a result of being overcome by fumes in caravans fitted with flueless instantaneous water heaters. These deaths heightened concerns about the adequacy of fixed ventilation and flues provided for liquified petroleum gas (LPG) appliances and the consequent risk of carbon monoxide poisoning.

175 The Department of Trade and Industry (DTI) and HSE met with the National Caravan Council (NCC) and the British Holiday and Home Park Association to discuss the concerns. A plan of action was agreed to minimise risks by ensuring instantaneous water heaters in caravans available for rent and new caravans offered for sale were brought into line with the relevant British Standards. It was agreed that any necessary modifications should be carried out by 1 March 1992, in time for the main holiday season.

176 There is considerable overlap between consumer protection legislation, enforced by TSOs, and HSWA and its relevant statutory provisions, enforced principally by HSE and local authority enforcement officers from Environmental Health Departments. In particular, caravan manufacturers, and site operators letting out caravans are subject to the Consumer Protection Act 1987. Under the Act the caravans should be "reasonably safe" and published standards are relevant in deciding this. Equally, the letting out of caravans is subject to Section 3 of the HSWA, which covers the duties of employers to minimise risks to the health and safety of those other than their employees.

177 Because of the overlap of responsibility it was necessary to establish who should take the principal role in ensuring the plan of action was implemented by the agreed date. It was agreed that DTI should take the lead, using consumer protection legislation and that TSOs would, therefore, undertake the enforcement role.

ENFORCEMENT IN PRACTICE

178 The following account describes how the Trading Standards Department of Surrey County Council undertook the task of ensuring site operators met the required standards. It was decided that the task should be broken down into a number of stages: identify sites; prepare an advisory letter explaining the British Standard requirements; issue a press release; and finally visit all sites to inspect hired caravans with a view to enforcement if necessary and make owner/occupiers aware of the safety standards.

179 In order to obtain information on the number and location of sites and the pitches they contained, the TSOs contacted their colleagues in the environmental health departments of the district councils. Enforcement Officers from the environmental health departments have the duty of licensing sites for mobile homes and residential caravans and record the permitted number of pitches, together with the nature of use: residential, short stay or holiday. It was estimated that up to one fifth of the 5000 licensed pitches might be hired for holiday or residential use, but accurate figures were not available.

180 All sites were visited between December 1991 and 31 January 1992. Advisory letters were distributed and caravans offered for hire inspected. A press release was also put out in January to ensure wide awareness of the safety issues and the inspection campaign. 4242 caravans were found on 123 sites; of these only 162 (3.8%) were for hire, much fewer than expected. Twenty-seven of the hired caravans had water heaters which did not meet the British Standard requirements. In all cases owners responded to correction notices by completing the necessary modifications by the 1 March deadline.

The way ahead

LOCAL AUTHORITIES CONCERNS AND PRIORITIES

181 While local authorities are mindful of the need to give health and safety an ever higher profile, there continues to be a number of conflicting demands on their resources. This inevitably means that the level

of health and safety enforcement in some authorities will not compare favourably with that found in others. Priority planning of inspection must, therefore, continue to be an important component in the approach by local authorities to health and safety enforcement. While it will never make up for a lack of resources, it should ensure that those resources which are available are effectively targeted.

182 Local authorities were caught in the drive to complete the single European market by 1 January 1993. A number of EC directives and subsequent UK statutes have impacted upon the work of local authorities, and provided further areas of enforcement to compete with health and safety.

183 This is not to suggest that health and safety itself has been exempt from the attentions of the European Community. As mentioned earlier in this report, 1992 has seen the adoption of six major EC Directives on health and safety. These were converted into UK legislation which came into effect on 1 January 1993. Local authorities need to digest and understand these new Regulations and, more importantly, to explain them to employers and employees where, in some cases, there is still a complete lack of understanding of even the most basic health and safety requirements.

184 In order to promote consistency of enforcement of the new Regulations between individual local authorities and between HSE and local authorities, SHELA commended to LAs the approach adopted by HSE. The principles of that approach have now been incorporated into an agreed statement on LA enforcement, which is set out at Appendix 7.

185 Local authorities believe that there is a need to institute a co-ordinated and well publicised campaign to convey the issues surrounding health and safety to those persons and premises where awareness is low, but the risks are often high.

186 Training continues to be an important issue, dealing not only with the emerging legislation from the European Community but also with the demands of the new domestic legislation. For example, the Electricity at Work Regulations, and the Control of Pesticides Regulations which became a local authority concern from 1 April 1992. The field of health and safety is increasingly diverse and complicated and local authority inspectors require continuing training on a wide range of topics. The Local Authority Associations look forward to greater opportunities for their inspectors to join with colleagues from HSE in joint training initiatives. They feel also that the facilities and expertise within HSE could be utilised in other ways, and look forward to the continuing development of the partnership which already exists between them.

187 The current initiative to establish lead authorities is a radical and in some ways revolutionary step forward to deal with health and safety on a co-ordinated national footing. However, the Local Authority Associations realise that the pilot study must be fully evaluated before any long term decisions can be made, particularly with regard to the resource commitment required by local authorities.

188 Many of these concerns have been raised in previous reports and some of the returns received from local authorities continue to paint a gloomy picture, as highlighted by the following entry.

> "The principal point of comment is the difficulty in deploying field staff in the very important area of health and safety at work in a period when intense demands have been generated by other major statutes: the Food Safety and Environmental Protection Acts in particular. The demand created by these statutes, backed up by specific statutory obligation, has deflected attention from the health and safety sector, especially as it has not been realistic to secure additional staff in the light of current financial pressures on the council."

189   Nevertheless some authorities are more optimistic. Specialisation, computerisation and priority planning are seen by many as the way forward, as the following returns illustrate.

"A point of note is that this department specialised during the year and although the statistical return indicates a fall in the number of inspections achieved, this specialisation, together with a more enforcement oriented policy has had a great impact on health and safety compared with preceding years."

"Following reorganisation, the enforcement of health and safety legislation is now being given a higher priority than in previous years. A team of officers enforces the legislation with one member of staff dealing solely with health and safety at work. A pro-active approach to enforcement has been adopted and the department has instituted a prioritised inspection programme. Other initiatives have been undertaken to promote health and safety at work including a week long joint initiative with HSE."

"Following a restructuring in 1991 the department now has a separate health and safety section. This includes the council safety officer, who acts in an advisory capacity. This revised structure is currently being reviewed due to a higher than anticipated work load. However, although this has affected the enforcement work programme, inspections generally are increasing."

190   HELA and the Local Authority Unit are doing all they can to help local authorities through this difficult time. The aims and objectives of both are continually being refined to ensure they meet current concerns.

HELA priorities 1993/94

HELA's plan of work for 1993/94 is as follows:

- to support the lead authority pilot trials, evaluate them and consider the future of this approach for occupational health and safety enforcement in the local authority sector;

- to develop an enforcement policy for local authorities and consider the need for a local authority enforcement database;

- to develop a workplan for the implementation of a local authority enforcement policy on occupational health;

- to produce open learning training courses suitable for all health and safety inspectors and industry on subjects including the Regulations needed to implement the EC Directive on display screen equipment;

- to continue to produce advice and guidance on new legislation, including developments arising from European Community initiatives and to ensure that local authorities receive guidance on other priority issues;

- to improve the quality and quantity of data on accidents; and to maximise the number of voluntary returns by local authorities on the work they perform in the enforcement of health and safety legislation;

- to support the training of LA inspectors on new legislative requirements.

ACCIDENT CASE STUDIES

Fatal accidents

Sixty-two fatal accidents were reported to local authorities during 1991/92. They occurred in a wide range of work environments, but warehousing, leisure activities and residential care homes were particularly prominent. Over half of the fatal accidents involved members of the public.

It is particularly disturbing that so many of the accidents could easily have been prevented. A number of the dangers have been highlighted in previous local authorities reports and remedial measures are often simple and inexpensive. Even so, some employers continue to expose both their employees and members of the public to unnecessary risk. New powers given in 1992 enabling magistrates, and sheriffs in Scotland, to impose fines of up to £20 000 and to imprison for a period of up to six months for certain health and safety offences, may convince such employers that appropriate preventive measures should be applied.

TABLE 1:
Fatal accidents 1991/92: type of accident and employment status of victim

Kind of accident	Employee	Self-employed	YTS	Trainee	Member of public	Total
Contact with moving machinery or material being machined	2	1	0	0	0	3
Struck by moving including flying or falling objects	3	1	0	0	2	6
Struck by moving vehicle	5	0	0	0	5	10
Struck against something fixed or stationary	0	1	0	0	0	1
Injured while handling, lifting or carrying	1	0	0	0	0	1
Slip, trip or fall on same level	0	0	0	0	6	6
Falls from a height	10	2	0	1	11	24
Drowning or asphyxiation	1	0	0	0	5	6
Exposure to or contact with harmful substances	0	0	0	0	1	1
Exposure to fire	0	0	0	0	2	2
Contact with electricity or an electrical discharge	1	0	0	0	0	1
Other kind of accident	1	0	0	0	0	1
Total	**24**	**5**	**0**	**1**	**32**	**62**

For employees, warehouse and loading bay incidents continue to give rise to the greatest number of fatal accidents. Although vehicles are often involved, the following case studies also illustrate the importance of secure storage. Guidance is available in the HSE publication *Health and safety in retail and wholesale warehouses*[2].

CASE 1

A young office administrator was crushed beneath a fork lift truck while walking through a carpet warehouse.

Although warehouse management carried radios, the administrator would often enter the warehouse area to deliver messages. At the time of the incident she was returning from giving an urgent order to the warehouse manager.

Subsequent investigation, which involved an HSE Specialist Inspector, revealed a number of deficiencies, all of which could have contributed to the accident. These included: the lack of an overall policy on the safe use of fork lift trucks, in particular whether or not the vehicle should be driven on the left or right-hand side of gangways; the need to restrict access for non-essential personnel; and problems associated with restricted vision to the rear of the trucks due to the method of mounting the propane fuel cylinders. The latter problem had been brought to the attention of management three weeks before the fatality. One week before the accident they were also advised, by a local authority enforcement officer, about the provision of speed governors for the vehicles. The lift truck driver had been trained and his vehicle was in good condition.

Comment

This case demonstrates the need for employers to give careful consideration to all aspects of vehicle safety in warehouses. Comprehensive guidance on the safe use of fork lift trucks can be found in the HSE guidance booklet *Safety in working with lift trucks*[7]. Further useful information can be found in the HSE guidance note *Road transport in factories*[8].

CASE 2

An untrained temporary warehouseman was killed while driving a fork lift truck.

The employee had not been formally trained or authorised by the company to drive a fork lift truck. He had been put to work with an experienced employee on the construction of wooden packing

cases. Under the direction of the experienced employee, he was told to use a fork lift truck to transport goods into the warehouse. The normal route was blocked and he used an alternative means of access which involved driving down a slope with a 10% gradient. He was later found near the bottom of the slope with the fork lift truck lying on top of him.

Although it was company policy not to allow unauthorised employees to drive fork lift trucks, the accident investigation revealed that temporary employees had not been advised of the restrictions. Supervisors were aware that the rules were being abused. Keys were left in fork lift trucks, encouraging unauthorised use. Once again, an HSE Specialist Inspector gave technical advice, demonstrating the growing partnership between local authorities and HSE. The company was subsequently fined £20 000.

Comment

Accident data show that the majority of fatal accidents caused by the overturning of a fork lift truck were the result of no fork lift truck training, no restrictions on who should drive, or inadequate supervision. Information on the training of lift truck drivers can be found in the HSE publication *Rider operated lift trucks - operator training*[9].

CASE 3

One man died and two others were injured when the tail lift on an articulated trailer collapsed.

The vehicle was being used to transport large items of computer equipment. It was fitted with a tail lift of French design. The only instructions for the safe use of the lift were in French.

The trailer had been backed into a loading bay and the gap between the vehicle bed and loading platform had been bridged by using a combination of the tail lift and a dock leveller. Contrary to the manufacturer's instructions, the support legs for the tail lift were not in use. In addition, investigation revealed that both travel hooks for the tail lift had been subjected to mechanical damage. The use of the dock leveller meant that there was additional loading on the lift. At the inquest the jury returned a verdict of death through lack of care. The company which owned the vehicle went into receivership shortly after the incident.

Comment

An unusual accident and yet one which could easily have been prevented by proper training and maintenance.

CASE 4

An employee at a cold store was fatally injured when a five-high stack of racking and goods, weighing approximately 4 tonnes, collapsed onto him.

The type of racking used in the cold store is known as a pallet converter set, consisting of a standard wooden pallet with a free-standing metal leg attached at each corner. The whole unit is held together by a metal frame and braced with metal tie-bars. Each converter is a free-standing unit which may be loaded with up to 1 tonne of goods.

It is believed that the employee was removing frozen food cartons from the bottom converter of a stack of five when the collapse took place. Investigation revealed that the bottom two converters had been braced with fabric straps and not metal tie-bars. To make matters worse, the bottom converter was not a proprietary brand. It had been fabricated by a small local engineering company and had not been rated and tested. Both the company and one of its directors were subsequently prosecuted and fines and costs in excess of £7000 were imposed.

Comment

Any company wishing to use pallet converters should ensure that it is fully conversant with the guidance contained in the HSE publication *Health and safety in retail and wholesale warehouses*[2].

CASE 5

An employee working for a warehousing company was fatally injured by goods collapsing onto her.

The deceased was reported missing at the end of the working day. Her husband had arrived to collect her but no-one knew where she was. A search was initiated and she was found beneath a pile of boxes which had fallen from an adjacent stack. The boxes had been stacked the previous day to a height of nearly 4 m. The estimated weight of the stack was approximately 15 tonnes, of which about 5 tonnes actually fell. No attempt had been made to "key" the stack, which was obviously unstable as the lower boxes were mis-shapen due to crushing. The warehouse manager knew of the problem and was intending to arrange for the boxes to be restacked. Pressure of work prevented this. The investigation showed that this was not the first time collapses had occurred in the warehouse due to poor stacking.

Comment

Guidance on the safe stacking of materials is readily available. If this had been followed, the accident would not have occurred. Further information on the stacking of materials is contained in HSE booklets *Essentials of health and safety at work*[10] and *Safety in the stacking of materials*[11].

CASE 6

An experienced electrician was crushed to death when a large control panel fell on him during a lifting operation.

The electrician was supervising two colleagues in lifting the panel off wooden battens on the floor onto a wheeled trolley. The panel was 15 feet long, 6 feet high and weighed approximately 1 tonne. It was also top heavy.

Two 5 tonne capacity "bottle" jacks were used to lift one end of the panel. During the operation the panel suddenly fell forwards, trapping the accident victim from the neck downwards. Subsequent examination of the jacks revealed that one of them had two defects which could have caused it to fail. Both had been purchased second-hand and examination revealed that the defective jack had been dismantled at some time in the past and incorrectly reassembled. The company had no arrangements or safe system of work for handling control panels at the premises.

Comment

Heavy items of equipment should not be moved unless a competent person has assessed the situation and formulated a safe system of work which details the lifting equipment required; procedures to be followed, including provision of temporary supports; and requirements for specialised training/ instruction. All lifting equipment should be properly maintained and tested where necessary.

Last year's report explained how falls continue to make a substantial contribution to fatal accident numbers. It went on to say that many employers view this type of incident as a genuine accident about which little can be done, but then gave two examples which clearly demonstrated this was not the case and that accidents can be prevented. The provision of very simple measures, such as the fitting of window restraints, can save lives. Unfortunately, some employers continue to ignore this advice, as the following cases demonstrate.

CASE 7

A 90-year-old resident at a residential care home fell to her death from a first floor bedroom window.

The single bedroom window was of a double hung sash type. When last checked by staff on the night of the accident it was closed.

The patient had previously lived in a bungalow and had been found wandering the streets on several occasions. She was distressed after family visits and suffered from depression. A sleeping tablet had been taken prior to the incident.

CASE 8

A 63-year-old resident at a residential care home fell to her death from her first floor window.

Again the window involved was of the sliding sash type. It was capable of being opened to leave a gap of 36 inches.

The woman's medical history indicated that she used to be an alcoholic. She stayed in her room except for meal times. Following the incident the owner fixed blocks on all the sash windows in the care home so that they could only be opened to a height of 12 inches.

CASE 9

A 92-year-old resident at a residential care home fell from the first floor window of a room to the ground below.

The window was of the double hung sash type. The top sash was not capable of being opened because of excessive paint build-up.

All other windows at the premises had either been modified to restrict the extent of opening or were of a different style or location so as not to pose a risk of falling. The window involved in the accident was subsequently altered to prevent it from being opened more than 4 inches. This was done simply and cheaply, but effectively, by putting screws into the sash boxes.

Comment

Details of a similar fatality in a residential care home were given in last year's report. It is therefore all the more tragic that some home owners have yet to address this problem. With these incidents in mind, and the specific requirement on window safety in the new Workplace (Health, Safety and Welfare) Regulations, this is likely be a particular area of concern for local authority enforcement officers in the future.

CASE 10

An office worker overbalanced and fell to his death from a third floor window.

Unlike the previous incidents, this fatality occurred in a modern building fitted with windows which pivot vertically through 360 degrees. In order to open the window the deceased person stood on some trunking. He overbalanced and fell to his death three floors below.

Comment

This accident shows that those in control of premises need to assess window design to determine whether or not restraints are necessary. If they are, then they should be fitted without delay and maintained in good condition. The assessment should take account of particularly vulnerable groups, such as children and the infirm, and of means of access for opening.

CASES 11 AND 12

An 87-year-old resident in a residential care home died after falling down the cellar stairs.

The resident suffered from partial dementia. He was known for wandering around the building and knew that food was stored in the cellar area. The door to the cellar was locked but the key was hung outside.

In a similar incident, a female resident at another care home fell down the cellar stairs. Although normally locked, on this occasion the door had been left open.

Comment

Senior management in both homes had identified the danger associated with unauthorised access to the cellar but the preventive measures taken to eliminate that danger were not adequate.

CASE 13

A self-employed maintenance man fell 4 m to his death from a ladder while attempting to remove a Christmas decoration in the car park of a super store. He was working alone and the ladder was not secured in any way.

The decoration had been attached to the top of a lamp standard. A tower scaffold was available on site for working on lamp standards but it could not be used for 65 of the 130 units because they were positioned in shrub beds. It was therefore common practice for maintenance men and cleaners to use ladders.

Comment

Again the risk had been identified but the remedial measures were inadequate. Following the issue of a Prohibition Notice, a mobile hydraulic platform was purchased. Where ladders have to be used, guidance can be found in the HSE guidance booklet *Safe use of ladders, step ladders and trestles*[12].

CASE 14

A warehouseman fell to his death from a mezzanine floor when the guard-rail on which he was leaning collapsed.

The incident occurred at a wholesale tyre suppliers. The mezzanine floor was 6 years old. It had been designed by the wholesaler's head office and installed by a local firm. Edge protection consisted of middle and top guard-rails welded to 6 mm angle iron support stanchions. Various middle guard-rails had been removed, including those in the area of the accident, to enable tyres to be easily loaded onto the mezzanine floor from the top of delivery vehicles. The top rail failed under the pressure of the deceased leaning against it and he fell to the floor below. In addition, the design allowed for chains to be used instead of guard-rails at the ladder access point and the loading bay area, but no chains were present at the time of the incident. The company was fined £1000 and ordered to pay costs.

Comment

Details of the mezzanine floor were never submitted to the local authority under the Building Regulations and despite extensive enquiries the firm were unable to locate any original plans. Structures of this type must be properly designed if accidents of this nature are to be avoided. The integrity of edge protection should be maintained at all times.

LEISURE ACTIVITIES

Enforcement responsibility for leisure activities was transferred from HSE to local authorities on 1 April 1990. This has presented LA enforcement officers with a wide range of new challenges and problems.

CASE 15

A member of the public was killed while participating in an invitation stock car race at a speedway stadium.

The stadium had been used for speedway and stock car racing for about 12 years. The track was inspected and licensed by the Stock Car Racing Board of Control for Formula 1 racing. At the time of the incident an "outlaws" class meeting was being held.

The deceased person was one of a number of spectators who took part in a "ladies' invitation" race. It was her first experience of racing and she drove one of the "outlaws" class stock cars that had been used earlier in the day.

The investigation revealed no evidence of deficiencies in the track or the construction of the vehicle. It appears that the main contributory factor in the accident was driver inexperience. A proper helmet, harness and neck brace were being worn at the time of the incident. However, as the car was constructed so as to give maximum protection to the regular driver, persons of a different stature would have been exposed to a higher level of risk of injury.

Comment

A recommendation was made that the stock car racing fraternity reconsider the practice of allowing "invitation races" for persons without experience, particularly where high-powered stock cars are involved.

CASE 16

A young child drowned in the swimming pool of a sports and leisure club.

The club had three separate pools, one of which was outside. The main indoor pool was irregular in shape with a depth of 1.2 m over most of its area, but with a depth of 2.0 m at one end.

The child was with two friends who were accompanied by an adult. The youngster got into difficulties while the adult was at the club shop and the two friends were receiving swimming lessons. The swimming instructor was told that there appeared to be a body at the bottom of the deep end of the pool and attempted a rescue. Unfortunately, despite the efforts of a number of people, resuscitation procedures proved ineffective.

The investigation by the local authority revealed that although constant supervision of the pool by a competent person used to take place, recent changes had meant that this was not the case at the time of the incident. Following a complaint some months earlier, an enforcement officer visited the complex to look at pool safety. Because constant supervision was in force at that time, no action was taken over the indoor pool, but a prohibition notice was issued at the outdoor pool as supervision there was inadequate. The incident also called into question the club's emergency procedures.

The owners of this sports and leisure club failed to address safety issues in a full and systematic way. Details of the precautions to be taken and the emergency procedures required are given in the joint HSC/Sports Council publication entitled *Safety in swimming pools*[13].

GENERAL

Last year's report gave an example of a warehouse manager who was crushed while working beneath the raised body of a road sweeping vehicle. The comment section highlighted the importance of correct propping and, where necessary, protection of control systems or their isolation to prevent inadvertent operation. The next two cases re-emphasise the importance of such precautions.

CASE 17

A maintenance manager was killed when the raised "A" frame of a mobile crane fell on him.

The deceased person and an assistant were attempting to re-reeve a mobile crane. The work necessitated raising the "A" frame on its hydraulic rams. While the deceased person was feeding ropes through the "A" frame it suddenly fell on him, causing fatal injuries. No attempt had been made to prop the "A" frame in its raised position, although suitable timbers were readily available.

The crane was supplied with a handbook, but this did not contain any reeving instructions or information about safety during reeving. In addition, the employer of the deceased had no health and safety policy statement. Investigation showed that the controls for the hydraulic rams to the "A" frame could easily be inadvertently actuated during the reeving exercise, causing it to descend.

Comment

The site where the accident occurred was owned by a company with several similar operations throughout the UK. A health and safety booklet produced by the company's chairman back in 1978 clearly identified the dangers associated with working under parts of machinery which had not been safely packed with timber. One paragraph read:

> "Before working under any structure supported by a hydraulic ram, such as crane jibs, fork
> lift trucks and tipping vehicles, make certain you introduce a stout prop".

If the company had taken the trouble to follow the recommendations contained in its own safety booklet, then this accident could have been prevented.

CASE 18

A maintenance engineer was killed when he became trapped between the mast and cab of a fork lift truck.

The deceased person was employed by a company specialising in the maintenance of mechanical handling equipment. He had been asked to carry out a routine service to the truck, which was owned by a distribution warehouse. The work was taking place outside and to the rear of the warehouse.

On hearing screams, an employee from the warehouse raced to the scene. He saw a man standing on

the dashboard of the fork lift truck being crushed between the mast and the cab of the truck. It was later noted that the ignition key was inserted and the ignition switched on. The control lever which activates the mast and tilts it back towards the cab was positioned so that it could be inadvertently actuated by someone standing on the dashboard.

Comment

There was no evidence to suggest that the deceased person had not been properly trained to ensure his health and safety while servicing the fork lift truck. It is therefore assumed that in an attempt to save time or effort he used an unsafe system of work which led to this most unfortunate incident.

CASE 19

A customer died after falling through an open trap-door in the floor of a retail shop.

The trap-door had been left open while staff moved stock from the basement into the sales area. A customer entered the premises and fell through the opening onto the basement floor below. He died two days later from severe head injuries. The trap-door access had been provided for services only and should not have been used to move stock.

Comment

The franchisee in control of the premises was prosecuted and fined £3500 plus substantial costs. A safe system of work has now been introduced, which is designed to ensure that a guard rail is in position whenever the trap-door is in use.

CASE 20

A resident in a care home died after taking a bath from which she received 35% scalds to her legs, feet and buttocks.

The deceased needed frequent bathing because she wore a colostomy bag. She was placed in a chair lift and lowered into the bath by a night assistant. The temperature of the bath was not checked immediately beforehand.

The resident began to scream on contact with the water. At first the assistant did not realise there was a problem because the resident often reacted in this way. However, on testing the water with her hand, she found that it was extremely hot.

The resident was removed from the bath which was half emptied and then refilled with cold. She was then placed back into the bath and washed. The assistant realised that she was looking unwell and she and the home owner attempted some first-aid measures, although neither of them were trained. The resident died from the scalds received.

Comment

There can be fewer well recognised hazards than that of placing someone into a bath of scalding water. Testing with the elbow first is a procedure which is second nature to many. Even so, particularly in a work environment where time may be short, there is always the possibility that such checks will be forgotten. For this reason it is now recommended that thermostatically controlled mixer valves be fitted at these baths. HSE is due to publish general guidance on health and safety in residential care homes during 1993.

Accidents in retail

The retail sector represents 40% of the premises for which local authorities have enforcement responsibility. Unfortunately, this year's statistics show that both the number of accidents to, and the over-3-day injury rates for, employees in the sector are continuing to rise. There were 933 major injuries to employees in retail shops reported to local authorities during 1991/92. A total of 10 172 injuries to employees were reported, of which two were fatal.

The greatest risk is encountered in warehouses and loading bays. Last year's report concentrated on these areas, so this year other aspects of health and safety in the retail sector are examined.

ACCIDENTS INVOLVING SHOPPING TROLLEYS

Elsewhere in the report (paragraphs 67 to 69) details are given of the work which has been done by HELA on shopping trolleys. It explains how a new booklet has been produced which alerts both employers and the public to the safe use of shopping trolleys. The following incidents illustrate why this guidance was felt to be necessary.

The injuries sustained from shopping trolleys can be serious.

■ "Mrs . . . . had just passed through the check-out when another customer turned and

swung her trolley, striking Mrs . . . . and knocking her to the ground."

This customer fractured her right femur.

Many parents allow their children to push trolleys. Unfortunately, this can often lead to injury.

- " . . . . was pushing the shopping trolley. Her younger sister was sitting in the trolley seat and her mother was holding the front of the trolley to guide it. The mother let go of the trolley to have a look at some items. . . . . slipped on some polythene and pulled the shopping trolley onto herself."

  This 3-year-old girl suffered a broken right arm and a cut lip.

- "A young boy pushing a loaded trolley of goods around the store struck Mrs . . . . , causing her to fall heavily on the floor."

  This customer fractured her left hip.

Children often do not see danger - to them a shopping trolley can be just another toy. Parents therefore need to be constantly vigilant.

- "Two small children were climbing on the side of the trolley which then fell over on top of them."

  One of the children, a 5-year-old girl, suffered severe bruising and broke her right leg in this incident.

OTHER INCIDENTS . . . .

The retail sector suffers its fair share of accidents relating to slips, trips and falls and manual handling. This section, however, serves to highlight two less prominent categories which nevertheless need to be mentioned, the first because of the potential for harm and the second because of the nature of the injured person.

- ".... was reversing his delivery van in the shop car park. Mrs . . . . was in his blind spot and he knocked her over, running over her leg."

  This shopper suffered a broken left leg and bruised hip but this could so easily have been a fatality.

Every year serious incidents involving vehicles are reported. It is therefore important to remind employers of the need to assess transport and introduce a clear policy on transport safety which should include reversing of vehicles. Guidance on this subject is given in HSE Guidance Note GS 9 *Road transport in factories* [8].

- "The child came from the house into the shop area. He climbed onto the work top where the mincer was situated. Whilst no-one was watching he put his hand into the mincer and became trapped."

  This $2^1/_2$-year-old boy had his left arm amputated.

  Once again, this incident illustrates how children are often unable to see danger. All adults, be they employers, employees or members of the public, should take this into account when operating in or entering a work environment.

Accidents in the hotel and catering sector

During the past 6 years, the rate of over-3-day injury in this sector has risen substantially. The major injury rate rose by nearly 50% in the 4 years to 1989/90, dropping marginally in 1990/91, with a further rise in 1991/92.

2495 injuries to hotel and catering workers (employees and self-employed) were reported to local authorities during 1991/92. Of these there were 384 major injuries and 2109 over-3-day injuries. Two fatal injuries were reported.

HOT SURFACES AND HARMFUL SUBSTANCES

In most local authority enforced sectors the two main kinds of accident are slips, trips and falls and manual handling operations. However, for the hotel and catering industry, injuries resulting from contact with hot surfaces and harmful substances represent the second most predominant kind (almost a sixth of all injuries) for the year 1991/92. The following examples illustrate some of the dangers involved.

Many of the chemicals used in hotel and catering are toxic or corrosive, particularly when in concentrated form. As a result, extra care needs to be taken when decanting into smaller containers or diluting.

■ "Miss . . . . was filling up bottles for the domestic cleaners. She pulled the funnel out of the cleaning gel and some of the substance splashed into her left eye."

■ "The kitchen porter was pouring dishwasher detergent into a small tub when it splashed into his eye." Both of the above suffered severe irritation to the eye but fortunately no long-term damage.

Careful thought should be given to the way in which cleaners are stored and to their means of transportation.

■ "Whilst wiping a shelf under the dishwasher which contained drums of washing and rinsing detergents, an employee tried to remove one of the drums. The weight of the drum caused her to drop it on the floor. As it was full, the detergent splashed out of the top inlet hole onto her face."

■ " . . . . was carrying a bucket of sanitised water. He slipped and some of the solution came into contact with his face. His eyes were stinging so he was taken to hospital where they were washed out."

Oven cleaning, perhaps looked upon by many as a safe operation, gave rise to many of this year's reported eye accidents.

■ "Whilst cleaning the oven using gloves and X cleaner, a small amount of the cleaner splashed into . . . . 's eye. Although the eye was washed immediately, medical assistance was still necessary. . . . . had been trained in the use of goggles but she was not wearing them at the time of the incident."

■ "Whilst using oven cleaning chemical to clean the griddle he received a splash into his left eye. He suffered a chemical burn."

Similar problems exist when cleaning beer lines in public houses.

■ "The Deputy Manager was cleaning pipes in the cellar when pipe cleaner splashed into his right eye."

Sometimes other people's carelessness results in injury.

■ "Another member of staff had used neat heavy duty cleaner to loosen some stubborn stains on the bottle skip. The barman was unaware that the chemical was still present in the bottom of the skip. As he moved it the chemical splashed up into his eye causing chemical burns to the cornea."

Finally -

■ "Whilst cleaning the inside of the dishwasher . . . . was splashed in the face by dishwash detergent. Both goggles and gloves were supplied but not worn."

The dishwash detergent involved in this incident contained phosphoric acid, sodium hydroxide and other ingredients. Employees are often unaware that the solutions they are using are capable of causing significant harm. In its concentrated form, sodium hydroxide can cause irreversible damage to the eyes, even if immediate first-aid is given.

The above incidents highlight the need for employers to carry out an assessment of all chemicals in use. Where possible, those which involve risks should be replaced by safer alternatives. Where this can not be done, consideration should be given to purchasing in diluted form. Employees should be provided with appropriate protective clothing and supervision should ensure that it is always worn. Comprehensive training in safe working procedures and emergency procedures, including first aid, is essential.

Not all burns are associated with chemicals.

■ " . . . . and a waiter decided to carry a two-gallon pot of hot soup from the back kitchen to the main kitchen. . . . . slipped at the doorway and the soup splashed over her."

This waitress received severe scalds to her right hand and arm.

■ "An employee was cleaning behind units in the kitchen adjacent to the fryer. He slipped and grabbed the fryer causing it to topple. The contents spilt onto his back and legs."

This kitchen assistant received burns to his lower back and lower legs.

■ " . . . . was returning from the coffee machine to the back room when he slipped. He was carrying a bucket of hot water which cascaded over him."

This crew member suffered serious scalds to his upper torso and arm.

■ " . . . . was emptying hot oil out of the fryer into a plastic container. The container melted and the oil poured over . . . . 's left and right legs and feet causing serious burns."

The following incidents highlight other work situations which can lead to danger from chemicals.

■ "There was a problem with a smelly drain in the kitchen. As the manhole could not be removed it was decided to clean the drain using chemicals. Mr . . . . crawled under the table to put the chemical down the drain. The chemical was sodium hydroxide in crystalline form. As he poured the crystals into the drain there was an immediate reaction resulting in the chemical and water flying back into his face. He received severe burns to his arm and face."

■ " . . . . was emptying the old fat into a drum which had previously been used to hold a cleaning chemical. After a few minutes white fumes started coming out of the drum. These made . . . . start to cough and wheeze. He also had irritation to his eyes. An ambulance was called and he was detained in hospital over night."

FALLING OBJECTS

This is another kind of accident which causes a significant number of injuries. The causes vary, as illustrated by the following examples.

■ " . . . . was collecting stock. The top shelf of the movable shelving fell. It hit . . . . causing her to fall. She was unconscious for a time and was taken to hospital by ambulance, where it was discovered that she had fractured her elbow."

■ " . . . . was taking out equipment to lay up a function room. During the operation an overhead projector fell from a shelf onto his head and arm. He was concussed and taken to hospital where he was kept in over night."

■ "An employee was pushing a trolley of air larders. The top larder struck the safety hoop of a ladder to a mezzanine floor. It fell from the top of the trolley and hit the employee's head. He was knocked unconscious and taken to hospital."

OTHER INCIDENTS

In 1991/92, there were 134 knife accidents to employees working in the hotel and catering sector. Employees using knives require a high standard of training and, where necessary, they should be provided with appropriate protective clothing.

- " . . . . leaned over a work surface area where there was a knife wedged such that its point was situated over the edge of the work surface. As . . . . leaned over the knife entered his body."

  This commis chef received a severe wound to his stomach.

- " . . . . and two other kitchen staff were cleaning up at the end of a shift. One of the chefs who had a knife in his hand turned round to speak to . . . . The knife struck his hand causing the injury."

  This chef received a cut to the base of two fingers on his right hand. Microsurgery was required.

  Guidance on knife safety can be found in HSE booklet *Safety in meat preparation: guidance for butchers*[14].

Finally, perhaps the most well recognised danger in a kitchen is one which still gives rise to accidents.

- "As one waitress was coming out of the kitchen, she opened the door into . . . . 's path."

  This waitress had her wrist broken in two places. After the incident the employer erected a partition to stop similar incidents occurring in the future.

Accidents in the leisure and recreation industry

A number of leisure and sports activities are inherently dangerous. This does not mean that those in charge can afford to ignore health and safety. On the contrary, they need to make strenuous efforts to ensure that the levels of risk are kept as low as is reasonably practicable.

During 1991/92 a total of 639 accidents in the recreational and other cultural services (leisure) industry were reported to local authorities. Many of those injured were members of the public, of these 262 were major injuries and 7 were fatal.

HORSE RIDING

Responsibility for the enforcement of health and safety in this leisure activity was transferred to local authorities on 1 April 1990. It was soon recognised as a major area of concern for local authority enforcement officers and HELA asked for the subject to be included in the Local Authority Unit's Guidance Project. The resulting publication is expected to be available in 1993 (see paragraph 92). The following incidents illustrate the potential for harm involved in horse riding accidents and the difficulties faced by instructors and enforcers when considering rider safety.

- " . . . . was trotting a pony round the outdoor school. She tried to get the pony to canter. When the instructor gave verbal encouragement the pony moved forward sharply and bucked. . . . . fell off."

- " . . . . was working with the rest of the group in the indoor school when a loud noise on the gallery startled her pony. It ran off, unseating the rider."

Both of the above young girls suffered broken arms.

The following extract from an accident report must surely call into question the judgement of one instructor.

- "Mrs . . . . lost control of her horse through not riding it correctly. She panicked, screamed, and frightened the horse. It bolted, causing the others to follow".

This nurse suffered concussion and was kept in hospital over night. The ride was taking place in the middle of a public highway.

Riding school owners and operators need to take particular care to ensure that all tack is kept in good condition.

- " . . . . was riding on a hack. On the way back she allowed her horse to overtake another. Whilst trying to regain control the rein broke and she fell over the horse's shoulder."

This 16-year-old fractured her left wrist.

OTHER INCIDENTS

Playground equipment, such as slides and climbing frames at catering premises, public houses etc, gives endless fun to children of all ages. It would be very unfortunate if a steady stream of accidents meant that such equipment was no longer made available for use. It is therefore hoped that the manufacturers of the equipment, the people who control it, and parents of children who use it, will work together to ensure that the facilities are retained by doing all in their power to prevent further accidents. These usually occur either because of obvious defects in the equipment or deliberate abuse by youngsters who fail to appreciate the dangers.

- "A child was seen climbing up the outside wall of the slide. She fell a distance of approximately 5 m."

This 8-year-old girl fractured her left leg. The incident could obviously have resulted in a much more serious injury.

- "He came down the slide at speed and was unable to stop at the bottom. He hit his head on a log which was fixed to the ground close by."

This 6-year-old suffered a large swelling on the back of his head.

- "A child was climbing on the frame and fell, breaking his left forearm."

A notice attached to the frame, which was situated in the children's play area of a pub, said:

"Frame is faulty and falling down. Customers use frame at own risk".

Further examples of the lack of supervision are illustrated by the following two incidents.

■ "Children were on a tour of the zoo. . . . . climbed from one carriage of the train to another. She fell from the train and was then run over by it."

The 12-year-old suffered a fractured pelvis.

■ "He fell from the side of the pirate ship. He was unsupervised and playing on his own."

This 7-year-old boy broke his left ankle.

Sometimes equipment installed to prevent one dangerous situation creates another.

■ "The child was sitting in the front seat of a monorail ride. As the ride approached the landing stage she caught her left arm between the ride and the adjacent barrier rail."

This 6-year-old suffered a fracture to her left forearm.

All of the above incidents involved members of the public, but employees in the leisure industry are also at risk. The following examples illustrate why falls continue to give rise to a significant number of incidents.

■ "The injured person was placing equipment onto the electrics gallery floor. He was standing on the access ladder, but as this was too short he had to lift the equipment to head height. As he put the equipment down, it overbalanced and fell towards him. In avoiding it, he fell from the ladder, landing on the floor below."

This voluntary worker at a theatre broke his wrist.

■ "The Deputy Manager was using a bar stool whilst assembling promotional material at a bowling centre. Whilst dismounting from the stool it moved and . . . . collapsed on the floor. As he fell, he brought his full weight onto the stool, which in turn trapped his arm. He fractured both main bones in the arm."

■ "The Deputy Manager at an entertainment centre erected a mobile ladder on the dance floor. One of the locking pins for the ladder was defective. Whilst the Manager was on the ladder a colleague began to move it. The remaining pin sheared and the equipment collapsed."

This employee suffered multiple fractures to his pelvis and dislocated and fractured his shoulder.

3

A NATIONAL PICTURE
OF HEALTH AND SAFETY
IN THE LA SECTOR

Introduction

LA ENFORCEMENT

1   The statistical report continues the series of published local authority health and safety statistics. It presents a picture of LA activity in enforcing the law on health and safety at work across Great Britain. The statistics on LA activity are derived from annual health and safety returns made by local authorities. Last year's report described how LA enforcement was altered following the Health and Safety (Enforcing Authority) Regulations 1989, which came into force on 1 April 1990. These Regulations transferred premises to LA enforcement. The main activities involved in the transfer included:

   ■   the display or demonstration of goods at exhibitions;

   ■   cosmetic or therapeutic treatments;

   ■   sports, cultural or recreational activities;

   ■   church worship or religious meetings;

   ■   care, treatment (with certain exceptions, including veterinary surgeries), accommodation of animals.

2   Following the introduction of these Regulations, local authorities are now responsible for inspecting around $1\frac{1}{4}$ million premises. Retail shops accounted for 38% of premises, offices 19% and catering services 16%. A further 15% involved consumer and leisure and cultural activities where the bulk of the transferred premises are concentrated.

INJURY FIGURES

3   The sections on workplace injuries include the sixth set of statistics based on reports made by employees under the RIDDOR[1] system. The supplement to the 1990 Labour Force Survey confirmed that *non-fatal* injuries are substantially under-reported. The LFS provides estimates of the true level of workplace injury in Great Britain and in which industries under-reporting occurs. A sample survey like the LFS cannot provide information on how injuries happen or identify particular types of work environment where accidents occur. However, it does complement RIDDOR data on non-fatal reportable injuries. The statistics on RIDDOR provide an indispensible source of sector trends, kinds of accident and identification of relatively high risk industries.

4   Injury analyses for the LA sector in this report are therefore based on individual report forms sent by employers and others to local authorities, and copied by them to HSE. Local authorities copy the majority of injury reports to HSE. A description of the sources of local authority health and safety statistics is given in Appendix One. Numbers of injuries and injury rates for every industrial sector are given in Tables 33 and 34 of Appendix Three. A full account of the 1990 Labour Force Survey results appeared in the December 1992 edition of the Employment Gazette.

5   This report considers the latest RIDDOR data for 1991/92 and trends in the 6 years till then. There are two new main features.

[1]*Reporting of Injuries, Diseases and Dangerous Occurrences Regulations 1985.*

Profiles of accidents in

- ◆ catering activities;
- ◆ retail industry.

Further information derived from the 1990 LFS

- ◆ individual industries of the LA sector;
- ◆ rates of injury adjusted for part-time working.

Summary

6   STAFF RESOURCES SINCE 1986/87

- There were 1360 'Full-Time Equivalent' staff working on Health and Safety in 1991/92.
- The number of FTE staff is slightly lower than that in 1990/91 and 24% lower than in 1986/87.

7   MORE PREMISES

- In 1991/92 local authorities were responsible for enforcing health and safety in 1.2 million premises, a rise of 80 000 (7%) since 1990/91. The number is now 28% higher than in 1986/87.
- Of the 80 000 extra premises, 25 000 were in consumer/leisure services sectors and reflects a continuing transfer to local authorities under the Enforcing Authority Regulations.
- Each full-time equivalent HSW staff is now responsible for 904 premises, a rise of just over two-thirds in the 6 years to 1991/92.

8   TRENDS IN INSPECTION

- **In 1991/92, LA inspectors made 512 000 visits, up 24 000 (5%) on 1990/91.**
- LA inspectors made 9000 extra visits to retail shops (increase of 5% compared with 1990/91) and 16 000 extra visits to catering services premises (up 13%).
- ***Local authorities have handled the increase in premises by exercising priority inspection, having maintained their visit rates to premises of higher risk.***
- In 1991/92 each full-time equivalent staff, made an average of 376 visits to premises, a rise of 6% on 1990/91.

9   ENFORCEMENT WORK

During 1991/92

- 21 680 enforcement notices were issued, up by 66% on 1990/91.
- 514 prosecution hearings were completed; this is 18% more than in 1990/91.
- The rate of complaints investigated per full-time equivalent staff, has more than doubled in the 6 years to 1991/92. The rate of enforcement notices has risen $3^1/_2$ times.
- 21 300 complaints were investigated, down 3% on 1990/91.

10 REPORTED INJURIES 1991/92

- 24 205 injuries were reported to local authorities. Of these, 4331 were major injuries and 62 were fatal injuries.

- There were 1935 injuries to members of the public including 32 fatal injuries.

- 45% of reported injuries were in retail distribution, the largest employing industry in the LA sector.

- Slips, trips, falls on the same level and falls from a height accounted for about two fifths of all injuries and three quarters of major injuries. They accounted for nearly 90% of injuries to members of the public.

- Handling, lifting and carrying accounted for 27% of all injuries.

- The highest rates of major injury are in the recreational (a component of the consumer/personal industry (see paragraph 45)) and wholesale sectors. The rate of major injury in recreational services is 55.7 (injuries per 100 000 employees), almost 80% more than the average of 31.6 for the LA sector as a whole. The rates for retail and wholesale distribution are 41.0 and 46.1 respectively.

- Retail distribution and social welfare (a component of the consumer/personal industry) have the highest rates for over-3-day injuries. The rate of over-3-day injury in retail distribution is 404.1, almost 70% above the average of 242.2 for the LA sector. The rate in social welfare is 303.6, a third above the average.

- The number of injuries per FTE staff has doubled between 1986/87 and 1991/92.

11 UNDER-REPORTING AND PART-TIME WORKING

- The extent of under-reporting of injuries and part-time working in the services industries means that rates of injury are substantially understated for the local authority sector - according to research from the 1990 Labour Force Survey.

Expressed per full-time equivalent employee:

- **working in retail, wholesale and hotel and catering industries has over four-fifths of the risk in manufacturing as a whole;**

- working in social welfare and recreational services has at least the same risk as in manufacturing as a whole;

- in retail and hotel and catering jobs, the risk of injury to part-time employees is 50% higher than full-time employees.

12 FATALITIES IN THE PAST 6 YEARS

- 138 employees and self-employed people have died while working in LA enforced premises.

- Falling from a height and being struck by a vehicle are still the commonest causes of deaths.

- 144 members of the public died on LA enforced premises.

- Falls from a height, (downstairs, out of other equipment) and slip, trip, fall accidents on the same level are the commonest causes of death.

- The rate of fatal and major injuries to employees has remained steady in the LA sector overall, and shows no real trend.

- In the hotel and catering industry, the rate of major injury is 54% higher than in 1986/87, reflecting a worsening trend in rate of slipping and falling injuries.

- **During the past 6 years the rate of over-3-day injury has risen substantially in all main industries of the local authority sector. This appears to reflect worsening performance rather than better reporting of injuries.**

- In the last 4 years there has been a steady rise in the number of reported major injuries to members of the public.

- Accidents to members of the public mainly occur in shops, hotels, restaurants and in "other residential accommodation".

- Figure A illustrates the numbers and rates of injury by industries subject to LA enforcement.

TABLE 1:
Summary of LA health and safety statistics for Great Britain

	For the year			Change 1990/91
	1986/87	1990/91	1991/92	1991/92
Number of premises	958 000	1 150 000	1 230 000	+ 7 %
Visits made by LA inspectors	567 000	488 000	512 000	+ 5 %
- of which, full HSW inspections	327 000	247 000	262 000	+ 6 %
'Full-Time Equivalent' HSW staff	1780	1370	1360	- 1%
(professional and technical)				
Complaints investigated	12 960	22 040	21 300	- 3 %
Enforcement notices issued	8100	13 030	21 680	+ 66 %
Prosecution cases completed	401	434	514	+ 18 %
Injuries reported under RIDDOR	14 348	23 868	24 205	+ 1 %
- of which, major injuries	2584	4268	4331	+ 1 %
Rate of all reported injuries in	188.8	245.3	274.2	+ 12 %
main local authority industries*				
(including consumer/personal)				
- of which, major injuries	29.1	31.2	31.6	+ 1 %

*Rate of injury is expressed per 100 000 employees and includes the relatively few fatalities, see paragraph 55
Key points are illustrated in Figures A and B.

FIGURE A:
Injuries to employees (including trainees) and incidence rates 1991/92

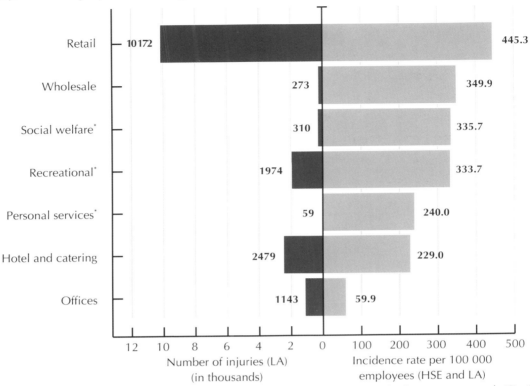

* Social welfare, recreational and personal services are part of the consumer/personal industry (see paragraph 45) - the number of injuries in these areas are increasing.
Based on Table 34

FIGURE: B
Summary of Health and Safety statistics. Change since 1990/91

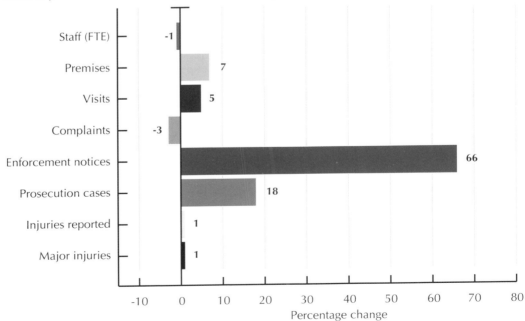

(LAE 1 data grossed up from 404 returns)
Based on Table 1

14   The figures in this section of the report are national estimates of premises, visits and enforcement action for the whole of the LA sector in Great Britain, for the year 1 April 1991 to 31 March 1992. The estimates are derived from the annual health and safety return (LAE 1 form) provided by 404 LAs (fuller details are given in Appendix One). A list of those local authorities that returned the 1991/92 form is in Appendix Four.

PREMISES

15   In 1991/92, local authorities were responsible for enforcing health and safety in around 1 230 000 premises. Retail shops continue to form the largest category of premises (38%) with offices and catering services accounting for 19% and 16% respectively (see Figure C).

FIGURE C:
Type of premises in the LA sector 1991/92

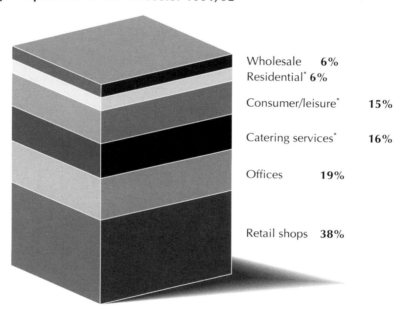

Wholesale **6%**
Residential* **6%**

Consumer/leisure* **15%**

Catering services* **16%**

Offices **19%**

Retail shops **38%**

* Type of premises is as defined on the LAE 1 form and differs slightly from the industries used in the section on injuries. (National estimates grossed up from 404 LAE 1 forms). Based on Table 2

16   Compared with 1990/91, the number of premises has increased by 80 000 or 7%. Of this rise, 25 000 was in the consumer/leisure service sector, 19 000 was in catering services premises and 17 000 in premises where the business was the provision of residential accommodation. Consumer/leisure services include premises where the main activity is recreational, sporting, cultural or other consumer activities such as beauty treatment and heel bars. It is defined by the types of consumer services and other premises and leisure and cultural services on the LAE 1 form. Type of premises is as defined on the LAE1 form and differs slightly from the industries used in the section on injuries.

TABLE 2:

Premises enforced by local authorities 1991/92, and changes since 1986/87 and 1990/91

Type of premises	Number of premises			Change 1986/87 - 1991/92	Change 1990/91 - 1991/92
	1986/87	1990/91	1991/92		
Retail shops	423 000	455 000	471 000	+ 11 %	+ 4 %
Offices	202 000	241 000	235 000	+ 16 %	- 2 %
Catering services*	130 000	175 000	194 000	+ 49 %	+ 11 %
Consumer/leisure*	84 000	154 000	179 000	+ 113 %	+ 16 %
Wholesale, warehouses, etc	63 000	63 000	72 000	+ 14 %	+ 14 %
Residential accommodation*	48 000	62 000	79 000	+ 65 %	+ 27 %
All premises	**958 000**	**1 150 000**	**1 230 000**	**+ 28 %**	**+ 7 %**

* Type of premises is as defined on the LAE 1 form and differs slightly from the industries used in the section on injuries.

17   With the exception of offices, the number of premises has increased in all types since 1990/91, with a 27% rise in the number of residential accommodation premises. The number of consumer/leisure services premises rose by 16%.

Of the 80 000 increase in premises between 1990/91 and 1991/92:

■   25 000 was for consumer/leisure services premises (just under a third of the total);

■   19 000 was for catering services;

■   17 000 was for residential accommodation;

■   16 000 was for retail shops;

■   9000 was for wholesale, warehouses etc;

■   there was a drop of 6000 in the number of office-based premises.

Changes in the number of premises since 1990/91 are shown in Figure D.

FIGURE D:

Change in the number of premises in the LA sector 1990/91-1991/92

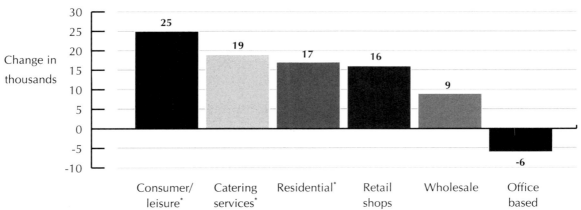

* Type of premises is as defined on the LAE 1 form and differs slightly from the industries used in the section on injuries.
For 1991/92, national estimates grossed up from 404 LAE 1 forms.
For 1990/91, national estimates grossed up from 400 LAE 1 forms.
Based on Table 2

The number of consumer/leisure premises rose by 25 000 in 1991/92 bringing the total rise to about 79 000 during the 2 years following the Enforcing Authority Regulations (in force from 1 April 1990). Allowing for previous trends in these premises, the number of transferred premises is estimated to have been about 50 000.

18   Growth in other premises has been strongest in residential accommodation (mainly due to the rise between 1990/91 and 1991/92) with smallest percentage growth in retail and wholesale premises.

Over the past 6 years (1986/87-1991/92) there has been:

■ a 28% rise in the number of premises, to 1 230 000;

■ an increase in the number of premises for all types although there was a decrease in the number of offices between 1991/92 and 1990/91;

■ an increase in the number of premises for consumer/leisure services, more than doubling to 179 000;

■ a 65% rise in the number of residential accommodation premises - the number of catering services premises went up by 49%.

19   There were 5920 local authority inspectors who were authorised to carry out health and safety and other work, in 1991/92. Most of these inspectors will have combined health and safety with other public protection work, especially inspections involving food hygiene. Some LAs also appoint other professionally qualified, and technical staff to carry out health and safety work. Often these staff do not have all the powers, particularly those relating to enforcement, which are available to inspectors under the HSW Act.

20   In 1991/92:

■ there were 1360 qualified staff (inspectors, professional and technical) undertaking health and safety duties at a full-time level;

■ 400 staff worked exclusively on HSW duties.

Table 3 shows the number of staff from 1986/87 to 1991/92

21   Since 1986/87

■ the number of authorised inspectors has remained fairly steady;

■ there has been a 24% drop in the full-time equivalent number of staff.

TABLE 3:
Changes in LA staff resources since 1986/87

| | Number of staff | | | Change |
Staff resources	1986/87	1990/91	1991/92	1986/87 - 1991/92
Authorised inspectors	5950	5910	5920	small change
Full-time equivalent number of qualified staff*	1780	1370	1360	- 24 %
Qualified staff working exclusively on HSW duties	420	370	400	- 5 %

* Authorised inspectors and other professional and technical staff undertaking HSW duties.

22   During 1991/92 local authorities made over half a million visits in connection with their health and safety duties, half of which were planned general inspections, involving a full inspection of the premises or a general overall assessment of health and safety. In 1991/92 there were:

- 512 000 visits in connection with health and safety duties;
- 262 000 planned general inspections (51% of all visits);
- 110 000 revisits to check, 32 000 planned special surveys or visits connected with enforcement initiatives and 108 000 'other' visits.

Figure E shows the overall number of visits broken down by type. The 'other' visits category has been subdivided into investigation of accidents, investigation of complaints, advice or training and visits to new businesses.

FIGURE E:
Visits connected with the HSW Act in LA sector 1991/92

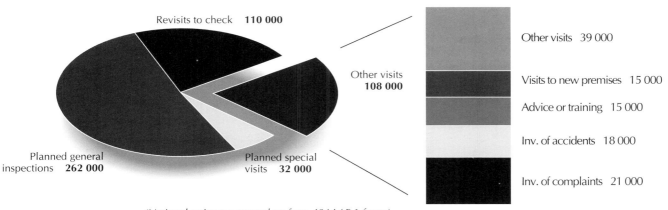

Revisits to check   **110 000**

Other visits **108 000**

Planned general inspections   **262 000**

Planned special visits   **32 000**

Other visits   39 000

Visits to new premises   15 000

Advice or training   15 000

Inv. of accidents   18 000

Inv. of complaints   21 000

(National estimates grossed up from 404 LAE 1 forms)
Based on Table 4

23   Compared with 1990/91:

- 24 000 more visits were made (up by 5% to 512 000);
- there was an increase of 6% in the number of planned general inspections (up from 247 000 to 262 000);
- there was an increase in the number of revisits to check by 8% (up from 102 000 in 1990/91 to 110 000 in 1991/92).

Changes in the number of visits between 1990/91 and 1991/92 are displayed in Table 4.

24   LA inspectors made more visits in 1991/92 than in 1990/91 and there were increases in both proactive and reactive types. Figure F shows the change 1990/91-1991/92 in the number of proactive and reactive visits, by type of premises. Proactive visits include planned general inspections, planned special visits and revisits to check. Reactive visits include investigation of accidents or complaints, advice or training, visits to new businesses and other visits.

For most types of premises there has been an increase in both proactive and reactive visits. There has been an increase of 10% in the number of proactive visits to catering services premises.

Changes in visits made by type of visit since 1990/91

| | Number of visits | | Change 1990/91- |
Type of visit	1990/91	1991/92	1991/92
Planned general inspection	247 000	262 000	+ 6 %
Planned Special visits	34 000	32 000	- 6 %
Revisits to check	102 000	110 000	+ 8 %
Other visits	105 000	108 000	+ 3 %
Total visits	**488 000**	**512 000**	**+ 5 %**

25   Following the introduction of the EA Regulations, there has been a change in the pattern of inspections. Table 5 shows the visits for the last 3 years.

■   *Inspectors made 24 000 more visits in 1991/92 than in 1990/91.*

■   *There were 16 000 more visits to catering services premises and 9000 more visits to retail shops.*

■   *Inspectors appear to have visited types of premises which were not visited last year due to visiting newly transferred premises.*

FIGURE F:
Visits connected with the HSW Act. Comparison 1990/91-1991/92 by type of premises

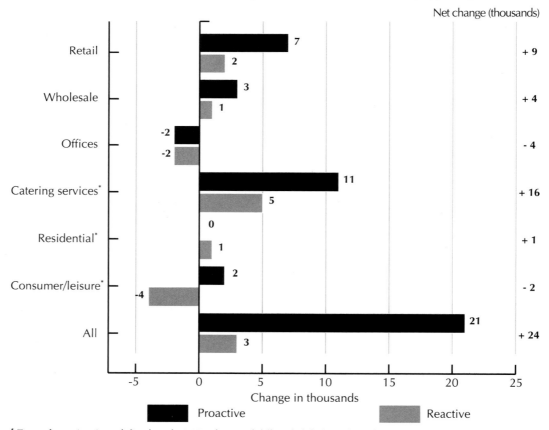

Net change (thousands)

Change in thousands

* *Type of premises is as defined on the LAE 1 form and differs slightly from the industries used in the section on injuries.*

TABLE 5:
Changes in visits by type of premises

Type of Premises	Numbers of visits (thousands)			Change in visits (thousands)	Change in premises (thousands)
	1989/90	1990/91	1991/92	1990/91-1991/92	1990/91-1991/92
Retail shops	184	178	187	+ 9	+16
Wholesale, warehouses	33	33	37	+ 4	+ 9
Residential accommodation*	35	30	31	+ 1	+17
Catering services*	126	120	136	+16	+19
Offices	50	51	47	- 4	- 6
Consumer/leisure*	43	76	74	- 2	+25
All visits	**471**	**488**	**512**	**+ 24**	**+80**

* Type of premises is as defined on the LAE 1 form and differs slightly from the industries used in the section on injuries.

26 The rate at which different types of premises in the LA sector are visited varies widely. It should be borne in mind that most LA health and safety enforcement officers work in Environmental Health Departments, which have a wide range of public protection duties, for example food safety and environmental protection. For certain premises LA inspectors combine HSW inspections with visits connected with their other duties. Figure G shows the rate of visiting for each type of premises for 1991/92.

FIGURE G:
Number of visits per 100 premises in LA sector 1991/92

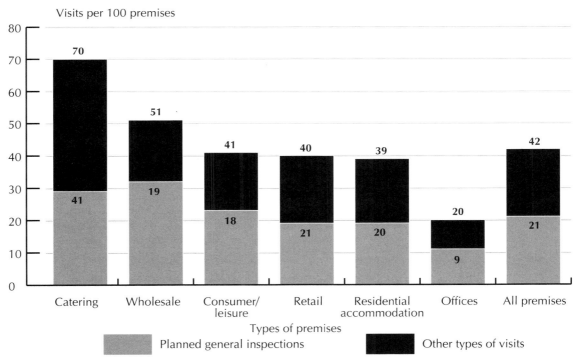

Visits per 100 premises

Type of premises is as defined on the LAE 1 form and differs slightly from the industries used in the section on injuries.
(National estimates grossed up from 404 LAE 1 forms).
Based on Table 6

27   Despite the increase in the number of visits in the last 2 years, during the 6 year period to 1991/92, the total number of visits and (planned) general inspections has decreased by 10% and 20% respectively. In percentage terms the greatest decrease analysed by type of premises occurred in offices and retail shops. However, comparison with 1989/90 before transfer of premises reveals that the rate of visiting per FTE staff has been:

   ■ going up in retail, wholesale and consumer/leisure services premises and
      catering premises;

   ■ maintained in offices;

   ■ reduced in residential accommodation premises.

Local authorities have maintained their visiting effort in premises of higher risk (to employees), and appear to have exercised priority in accordance with risk. Table 6 shows the visit rate per 100 premises, analysed by type of premises.

TABLE 6:
Changes in visits made per 100 premises, since 1986/87

| | Number of visits per 100 premises | | | |
Type of premises	1986/87	1989/90	1990/91	1991/92
Catering services	100	82	69	70
Wholesale shops, warehouse, etc	60	54	52	51
Consumer/leisure*	62	43	49	41
Residential accommodation*	67	60	48	39
Retail shops*	62	41	39	40
Offices	36	23	21	20
All premises	**60**	**45**	**42**	**42**

Type of premises is as defined on the LAE 1 form and differs slightly from the industries used in the section on injuries.

28   In 1991/92 each full-time equivalent member of staff made 376 visits; the figure for 1990/91 was 356. The rate of visiting per full-time equivalent inspector reveals no trend in the 3 years to 1989/90. The rate has risen steadily since then.

29   Figure H illustrates the trends in local authority visits expressed per full-time equivalent staff and per 1000 registered premises.

   ■ On average each full-time equivalent staff visited 15% more premises than 2 years ago.

   ■ Fewer staff and increased numbers of premises means a declining trend in the visit rate per 1000 premises.

LETTERS AND ENFORCEMENT NOTICES

30   During 1991/92 LA inspectors issued 21 680 formal enforcement notices, of which 88% were improvement notices. Of the formal notices, there were:

FIGURE H:
Visits carried out by LA inspectors 1991/92

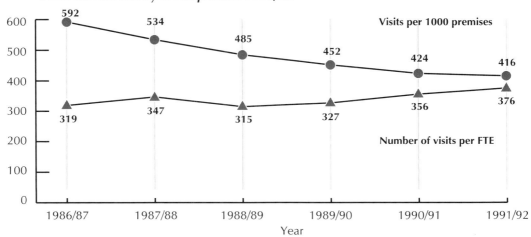

- 18 980 improvement notices;
- 2410 immediate prohibition notices;
- 290 deferred prohibition notices.

In 1991/92, 138 780 letters asking for compliance were issued. Between 1990/91 and 1991/92 the number of formal notices rose by 66%.

31   During the past 6 years the number of improvement notices rose by almost 3 fold with immediate prohibition notices more than doubling. This increase in the number of improvement notices was mainly due to the large increase between 1990/91 and 1991/92. Deferred prohibition notices went down by 3%, though the number of such notices issued is relatively small. Changes in the number of formal notices are given in Table 7.

TABLE 7:
Changes in formal notices issued 1986/87-1991/92

Type of formal notice	Number of formal notices issued			Change 1986/87 - 1991/92
	1986/87	1990/91	1991/92	
Improvement	6740	10 590	18 980	+ 182%
Deferred prohibition	300	240	290	- 3%
Immediate prohibition	1060	2200	2410	+ 127%
All formal notices	**8100**	**13 030**	**21 680**	**+ 168%**

PROSECUTIONS

32   The number of completed prosecutions fluctuates from year to year, but during 1991/92, Inspectors completed 514 prosecution cases (up 28% compared with 1986/87). Of these:

- 374 were mainly under the Health and Safety at Work Act (73% of the total);
- 92 were mainly under Regulations;
- 29 were mainly under the Offices, Shops and Railway Premises Act.

33 Each prosecution case can consist of more than one information laid, ie a 'charge' (in Scotland a complaint taken by the 'Procurator Fiscal'). By comparing the number of informations laid with the number of convictions, we can obtain the conviction rate for each type of legislation.

TABLE 8:
Prosecution cases completed

	Number of cases completed			Change 1986/87-
Legislation	1986/87	1990/91	1991/92	1991/92
Health and Safety at Work Act	297	325	374	+ 26 %
Offices,Shops and Railway Premises Act	51	39	29	- 43 %
Regulations	33	67	92	+ 179 %
Other legislation*	20	3	19	- 5 %
All prosecution cases	**401**	**434**	**514**	**+ 28 %**

* Including the Factories Acts

TABLE 9:
Conviction rates by type of legislation

Type of legislation	Conviction rate
Health and Safety at Work Act	89%
Offices,Shops and Railway Premises Act	85%
Regulations	91%
All informations laid	88%

Injuries reported under RIDDOR 1991/92

34 In 1991/92, a total of 24 205 injuries were reported to local authorities and copied to HSE's Local Authority Unit. We would like to thank local authorities for their continued co-operation in sending in the F2508 forms. A full description of the sources of LA health and safety statistics, with statistical tables, are given in Appendices One, Two and Three.

35 In 1991/92 there were:

- 22 125 injuries to employees (including trainees);
- 1935 injuries to members of the public;
- 145 injuries to the self-employed;
- 62 fatal injuries;
- 25 fatal injuries to employees;
- 32 fatal injuries to members of the public.

Of the 22 125 injuries reported to employees, almost 90% were over-3-day injuries. Table 10 shows injury statistics by employment status and severity of injury.

TABLE 10 :
Employment status and severity of injury 1991/92

Status of injured person	Fatal	Severity of injury*		Total
		Major	Over-3-day	
Employee (including trainees)	25	2368	19 732	22 125
Self-employed	5	60	80	145
Member of public	32	1903	†	1935
Total	**62**	**4331**	**19 812**	**24 205**

* As defined in RIDDOR   † Not reportable

36 Of the 24 205 injuries reported in 1991/92:

■ 30% were caused by slip, trip or fall on the same level;

■ 27% were caused by handling, lifting, carrying;

■ just over three-quarters of major injuries and nearly half of fatal were from slip, trip, fall on the same level or falls from a height;

■ 45% occurred in retail distribution;

■ 12% occurred in hotel and catering industries;

■ 19% occurred in warehouse and storage environments, with a further 8% in wholesale industries;

■ 29% of fatal injuries occurred in the residential areas of premises;

■ 18% occurred in sporting activity environments.

More detailed statistics on kind of accident, industry activity and environment for all employment statuses are given in Tables 28, 29 and 30 of Appendix Three.

37 Since the introduction of RIDDOR in 1986/87, the number of injuries reported to local authorities has increased by 69%. However, the bulk of these injuries are to employees for whom rates of injury are a more reliable indicator of performance.

38 Since 1986/87, the number of reported injuries to members of the public has been steadily increasing. There were 780 reported injuries in 1986/87 and this had more than doubled to 1935 in 1991/92. The number of injuries in the hotel and catering industries has gone up from 213 to 489. The number in the retail industry has risen by 50% since 1986/87.

TABLE 11:
Injury trends for the first 6 years of RIDDOR: injuries to employees (including trainees), self-employed and members of the public.

Severity of injury	Number of Injuries				Change 1986/87- 1991/92
	1986/87	1989/90	1990/91	1991/92	
Major	2584	3569	4268	4331	+ 68%
Over-3-day	11 731	18 166	19 545	19 812	+ 69%
All injuries*	14 348	21 796	23 868	24 205	+ 69%

* Includes fatal injuries

TABLE 12:
Injury trends per full-time equivalent staff, 1986/87-1991/92

	1986/87	1987/88	1988/89	1989/90	1990/91	1991/92
Number of injuries per FTE	8.1	10.9	11.6	15.1	17.4	17.8

Table 12 shows that the numbers of injuries per FTE staff has been increasing since 1986/87, the figure is now over double that in 1986/87.

Injuries to employees 1991/92

39   This section of the report concentrates on the number of injuries to employees. It includes injuries to those on government training schemes. Trends in rates are discussed at paragraph 44.

In 1991/92 there were 22 125 injuries to employees. Of these:

■   *25 were fatal injuries;*

■   *2368 were major injuries;*

■   *19 732 (89%) were over-3-day injuries;*

■   *46% of employee injuries occurred in retail distribution;*

■   *11% occurred in hotel and catering;*

■   *10% occurred in postal services;*

■   *9% occurred in wholesale distribution;*

■   *5% occurred in office-based industries.*

40   The kind of accident classification describes the impact of accidents on people. Analysis by kind of accident (in Table 13) reveals:

TABLE 13:
Kind of accident and severity of injury 1991/92. Employees (including trainees)

Kind of accident	Fatal	Severity of injury		Total
		Major	Over-3-day	
Handling, lifting carrying	1	137(6%)	6470(33%)	6608(30%)
Slip, trip, fall (same level)	-	1078(46%)	4707(24%)	5785(26%)
Struck by a moving or falling object	3	168(7%)	2704(14%)	2875(13%)
Fall from a height	11	528(22%)	1594(8%)	2133(10%)
Struck by a moving vehicle	5	116(5%)	1453(7%)	1574(7%)
Struck against something fixed	-	88(4%)	1207(6%)	1295(6%)
Hot surfaces and harmful substances	-	113(5%)	637(3%)	750(3%)
Contact with moving machinery	2	60(3%)	499(3%)	561(3%)
Other	3[*]	80(3%)	461(2%)	544(2%)
Total	**25**	**2368**	**19 732**	**22 125**

Percentages are shown in brackets and may not total 100% due to rounding.
[*] Includes one fatal caused by contact with electricity or an electrical discharge, and one by drowning or asphyxiation.

- handling, lifting, carrying accidents accounted for 6608 or 30% of injuries to employees. Most of these were by handling, lifting or carrying heavy or awkward/sharp objects;

- slips, trips or falls on the same level caused 26% of all accidents (5785). Three-fifths of these were from either slipping on a slippery surface or a person losing their footing for no apparent reason or stepping out of a vehicle and landing awkwardly;

- being struck by a moving or falling object was responsible for 2875 or 13% of all injuries;

- falls from a height accounted for 2133 or 10% of injuries to employees.

Slips, trips or falls on the same level accounted for nearly half of major injuries.

Falling from a height accounted for just over a fifth of major injuries.

Figure I shows the kind of accident causing major and fatal injuries, while Figure J is a corresponding graph for over-3-day injuries.

FIGURE I:
Kind of accident: Fatal and major injuries - employees (including trainees)

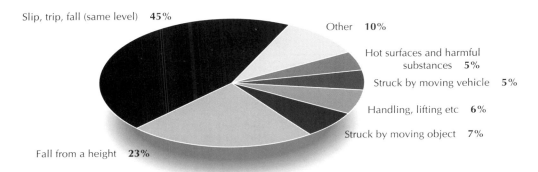

Slip, trip, fall (same level) **45%**

Other **10%**

Hot surfaces and harmful substances **5%**

Struck by moving vehicle **5%**

Handling, lifting etc **6%**

Struck by moving object **7%**

Fall from a height **23%**

Injuries in the LA sector 1991/92. Percentages may not total 100% due to rounding.
Based on Table 13.

FIGURE J:
Kind of accident: Over-3-day injuries - employees (including trainees)

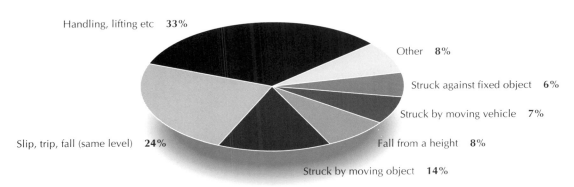

Handling, lifting etc **33%**

Other **8%**

Struck against fixed object **6%**

Struck by moving vehicle **7%**

Fall from a height **8%**

Slip, trip, fall (same level) **24%**

Struck by moving object **14%**

Injuries in the LA sector 1991/92. Percentages may not total 100% due to rounding.
Based on Table 13.

41   During 1991/92 there were 25 fatal injuries to employees. Eleven were caused from falls from a height. Five injuries were caused by being struck by a moving vehicle with a further three from being struck by a moving, flying or falling object. Slips, trips or falls on the same level were responsible for just under half of major injuries, with falls from a height causing 22%.

42   The main points for analysis by kind of accident within sector activities (shown in Table 14) are:

■   the pattern of injuries in the retail sector is similar to that in the LA sector overall (handling, lifting carrying 30%, slips, trips, falls (same level) 26%, struck by an object 15%);

■   34% of injuries in hotel and catering are caused by slip, trip or fall on same level. Just less than a fifth are caused by handling, lifting, carrying. About a sixth of accidents in this sector are from contact with hot surfaces and harmful substances;

■   57% of injuries to the employees in office based activities resulted from a slip, trip or fall on same level or from handling, lifting or carrying activities.

TABLE 14:
Kind of accident and industry, injuries to employees (including trainees), reported to LAs 1991/92

Kind of accident	Retail	Wholesale	Activity Hotel and catering	Office based	Consumer/ personal
Slip, trip, fall (same level)	2653(26%)	381(19%)	844(34%)	342(30%)	182(28%)
Handling, lifting, carrying	3045(30%)	581(29%)	450(18%)	304(27%)	168(26%)
Struck by a moving object	1485(15%)	280(14%)	303(12%)	142(12%)	51(8%)
Fall from a height	795(8%)	260(13%)	205(8%)	189(17%)	111(17%)
Struck by a moving vehicle	854(8%)	250(13%)	35(1%)	23(2%)	12(2%)
Struck against something fixed	691(7%)	100(5%)	102(4%)	65(6%)	17(3%)
Hot surfaces and harmful substances	214(2%)	20(1%)	399(16%)	20(2%)	29(5%)
Contact with moving machinery	264(3%)	78(4%)	67(3%)	27(2%)	19(3%)
Other	171(2%)	24(1%)	74(3%)	31(3%)	53(8%)
Total	**10 172**	**1974**	**2479**	**1143**	**642**

Percentages are shown in brackets and may not add up to 100% due to rounding.

43   Each workplace is likely to include a number of different physical environments. For instance a retail shop may have a sales area, a storage area, a loading bay, an office and a kitchen. It is useful to look at the environments where most accidents happen, independently of which types of premises are involved. More accidents occur in warehouse, storage and sales areas than in any other environment. During 1991/92:

■   4618 or 21% of injuries to employees occurred in warehouses or storage rooms;

■   2916 or 13% occurred in sales areas, with 2682 or (12%) of injuries occurring 'off the premises' with a further 2598 (12%) in loading bays;

■ 357 or 15% of major injuries occurred in warehouses or storage rooms, with 288 (or 12%) in sales areas and a further 291 (or 12%) 'off the premises';

■ 12 of the 25 deaths to employees occurred in warehouse, storage or loading bay environments or 'off the premises'.

TABLE 15:
Environment of accident and severity of injury, injuries to employees (including trainees) as reported to local authorities, 1991/92

ENVIRONMENT	SEVERITY OF INJURY			
	Fatal	Major	Over-3-day	Total
Wholesale/storage	5	357	4256	4618
Sales areas	-	288	2628	2916
Off premises - on delivery	4	291	2387	2682
Loading bays	3	226	2369	2598
Food preparation/kitchen	-	209	1599	1808
Offices	1	179	1047	1227
Stairs, corridors, etc	1	178	1030	1209
Post office - sorting room	-	24	652	676
Bars/restaurants	-	105	513	618
Residential areas	1	49	295	345
Staff room	-	62	236	298
Meat room	-	16	275	291
Cellar	-	13	269	282
Mail order	-	5	268	273
Car parks	-	50	212	262
Cold room	-	25	231	256
Bakery	-	34	200	234
Vehicle repair	-	10	102	112
Other environments	10*	247	1163	1420
Total	**25**	**2368**	**19 732**	**22 125**

* *Other environments includes 2 fatalities occurring in sporting activities, 1 in workshop/machine room, 1 in cold store and 1 in leisure/recreational environments. There were 5 fatal injuries in other environments.*

EMPLOYEE INJURY RATES FOR ACTIVITIES MAINLY ENFORCED BY LOCAL AUTHORITIES

44   Reported injury incidence rates for major and over-3-day injuries in 1991/92 are given in Tables 31 and 32 of Appendix Three for activities mainly enforced by local authorities. Table 34 gives injury rates for all industry sectors, analysed by severity of injury. The rates are expressed per 100 000

employees in employment. A note on the derivation of rates of injury is given in Appendix One. Paragraph 92 gives the effect of expressing injury rates per full-time equivalent employee.

45   As a result of the Enforcing Authority Regulations, local authorities also enforce health and safety legislation in certain additional consumer service industries such as recreational, and some social and personal services. This means that the consumer/personal sector now comprises three main industries:

■   social welfare including provision of residential care accommodation, professional organisations and religious bodies;

■   recreational, sporting and cultural services;

■   personal services, including hairdressing, heel bars, saunas.

46   Rates of injury for these and the traditional LA enforced industries are given in Figures K and L. The numbers do not take into account any under-reporting of injuries by occupiers of premises in either the LA or HSE enforced sectors (see paragraphs 3 and 4). The injury rates do, however, provide some indication of the relative degrees of risk in activities in the local authority enforced sector.

FIGURE K:
Injury rates for employees (including trainees) - major injuries 1991/92

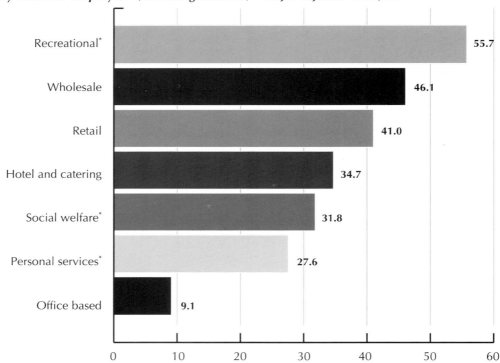

Social welfare, recreational and personal services are part of the consumer/personal industry (see paragraph 45) - the number of injuries in these areas are increasing.
Injuries reported to LAs and HSE and rates per 100 000 employees.
Based on Table 31

For major injuries, the highest rates are in:

■   recreational, sporting and cultural activities (55.7 per 100 000);

■   wholesale distribution (46.1);

■   retail distribution (41.0).

Injury rates for employees (including trainees) - Over-3-day injuries1991/92

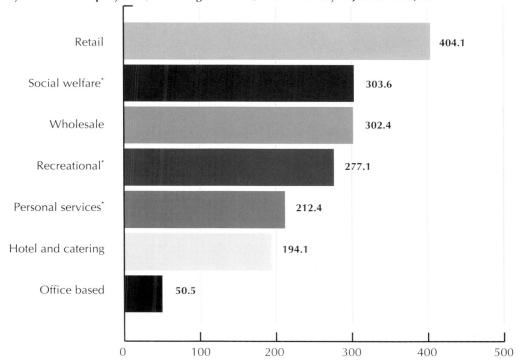

* *Social welfare, recreational and personal services are part of the consumer/personal industry (see paragraph 45) - the number of injuries in these areas are increasing.*
Injuries reported to LAs and HSE and rates per 100 000 employees.
Based on Table 32

By contrast, the lowest rates are in office-based activities at 9.1 per 100 000.

However, commonly occurring accidents such as slips, trips, falls (on the same level) and falls from a height still occur in offices.

47   For over-3-day injuries the highest rates are in:

■ retail distribution (404.1 injuries per 100 000 employees);

■ social welfare, professional organisations, etc (303.6);

■ wholesale distribution (302.4);

■ recreational, sporting and cultural services (277.1).

INJURY TRENDS 1986/87-1991/92 TO EMPLOYEES (INCLUDING TRAINEES)

48   The number of both reported major and over-3-day injuries has been increasing each year since 1986/87. To assess trends, however, we must derive rates of injury per worker. Since 1986/87 the number of people employed in the LA sector has increased by 13% or 1 million. There has been an increase in employment in all four main industries in the LA sector. The largest increase has been in office-based industries, where the number of employees has risen by 19% since 1986/87. The number employed in the retail sector has also gone up by 12%. Trends in rates of injury are given in Figures M and N.

49   The pattern of change in the number of reported injuries differs for the various activity groupings within the LA enforced sector. The number of injuries in the retail, wholesale, hotel and catering and office based activities are shown in Table 16. The number of injuries in consumer/personal service industries reflects the fact that premises of this type have only recently been transferred to LA responsibility and are given in Tables 31 and 32.

50   The 25 fatalities to employees in 1991/92 compares with a figure of 16 for 1990/91, and with 27 for the previous year. Numbers and rates of fatality reflect the natural variation in relatively small numbers of injuries.

Trends can more reliably be determined from the larger numbers of major and over-3-day injuries. For traditional activities subject to LA enforcement the rate of major injury per 100 000 employees was 29.9 in 1991/92, as compared with 31.2 in 1987/88, 29.3 in 1988/89, 30.6 in 1989/90, and 31.2 in 1990/91. The rate of major injury fell slightly from 1990/91.

FIGURE M:
Injury rates for employees (including trainees) - major injuries

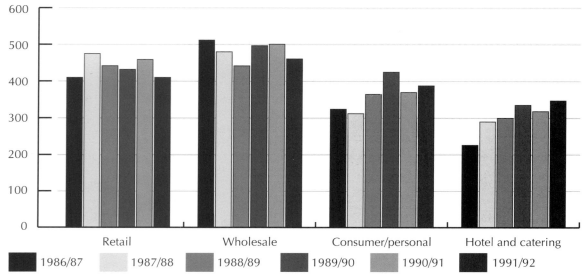

Injuries reported to LAs and HSE. Rate per 100 000 employees.
Based on Table 17

FIGURE N:
Injury rates for employees (including trainees) - Over-3-day injuries

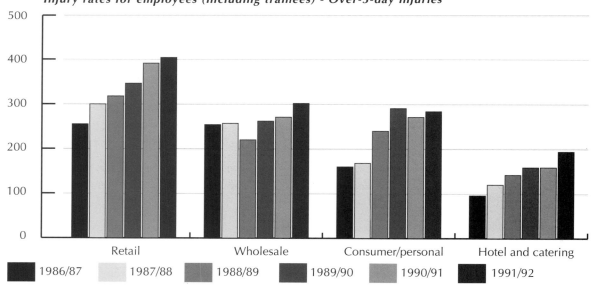

Injuries reported to LAs and HSE. Rate per 100 000 employees.
Based on Table 18

TABLE 16:
Injury trends by activity 1986/87-1991/92. Injuries to employees (including trainees)

| Activity | Number of injuries reported to LAs | | | | | | | |
| | 1986/87 | | 1989/90 | | 1990/91 | | 1991/92 | |
	Major	Over-3-day	Major	Over-3-day	Major	Over-3-day	Major	Over-3-day
Retail	814	5062	952	7703	1017	8697	933	9237
Wholesale	191	784	263	1411	282	1583	236	1731
Hotel and catering	190	777	349	1646	362	1786	374	2103
Office based	115	586	136	795	158	930	188	952
All above	**1310**	**7209**	**1700**	**11 555**	**1819**	**12 996**	**1731**	**14 023**

51 In contrast, the rate of over-3-day injuries for the LA sector as a whole has risen by 46% throughout the past 6 years. Any effect on trends of changing reporting levels is difficult to assess but there is no reason to suppose that better reporting accounts for the substantial rise in the rate of over-3-day injury.

TABLE 17:
Major injury rates for employees (including trainees)

| Activity | Major injury rates per 100 000 employees | | | |
	1986/87	1989/90	1990/91	1991/92
Retail	41.0	43.2	45.9	41.0
Wholesale	51.2	49.7	50.1	46.1
Hotel and catering	22.6	33.5	31.8	34.7
Offices	8.2	8.3	8.4	9.1
All above	29.1	30.6	31.2	29.9
Consumer/personal*	32.4	42.5	37.0	38.8

TABLE 18:
Over-3-day injury rates for employees (including trainees)

| Activity | Over-3-day injury rates per 100 000 employees | | | |
	1986/87	1989/90	1990/91	1991/92
Retail	255.1	346.1	391.4	404.1
Wholesale	253.9	261.6	271.3	302.4
Hotel and catering	95.6	158.9	159.8	194.1
Offices	40.8	43.5	47.9	50.5
All above	159.3	196.1	213.3	232.5
Consumer/personal*	160.2	290.8	271.5	284.4

* Consumer/personal sector includes social welfare, recreational, sporting and cultural services and personal services in which LA enforcement has been extended by the EA Regulations 1989. It has been shown separately because the transfer under these Regulations only took place in 1990 and therefore direct comparison with previous years is inappropriate.

52 The main features on trends during the past 6 years in rates of injury to employees include:

- rate of fatality has fluctuated with no discernible trend;

- no trend in rate of major injury for most industries subject to LA enforcement;

- in hotels and catering the major rate rose by 50% in 3 years to 1989/90 and is now at its highest level;

- a steady rise in the rate of over-3-day injury in most industries; as follows-

retail	58%	
wholesale	19%	
hotel and catering	103%	
office-based	24%	from a very low base
consumer/personal services	78%	

INJURIES TO SELF-EMPLOYED PEOPLE

53 In 1991/92 there were 145 accidents reported by the self-employed. Of these 78 (or 54%) were caused by falls from a height with 13 from handling, lifting and carrying and 10 were from being struck by an object. Of the 145 injuries, 80 were over-3-day injuries and 60 were major injuries. There were five fatal injuries.

Fatal injuries

54 This section considers the number of fatal injuries since the introduction of RIDDOR in 1986/87. Descriptions of the circumstances are given earlier in Part 2 of the report.

55 During the last 6 years (1986/87 to 1991/92), 282 people have died in LA enforced premises. Of these:

- 144 (or 51%) have been to members of the public;

- 138 (or 49%) to employees (including trainees) and self-employed;

TABLE 19:
Fatal accidents 1986/87-1991/92. Kind by employment status

Kind	Employees and Self-Employed	Members of the Public	Total
Fall from a height	51	58	109
Struck by a vehicle	35	14	49
Drowning/asphyxiation	4	22	26
Slip, trip, fall (same level)	3	21	24
Contact with machinery	14	7	21
Struck by an object	15	8	23
Other	16	14	30
Total	**138**	**144**	**282**

- 109 (or 39%) of all deaths arose from falls from a height;
- 49 (or 17%) of deaths were caused by being struck by a vehicle (this mostly affected employees);
- 26 (or 9%) of deaths were from drowning/asphyxiation (mainly members of the public);
- 201 (71%) of deaths have been to men and 81 (29%) to women.

56　Of the 138 fatal accidents to employees and self-employed people:

- about half (62) were in the retail and wholesale industries;
- just over a third (51) resulted from falls from a height;
- just over a quarter (35) resulted from being struck by a vehicle.

Falling from a height (particularly down stairs) and being struck by a vehicle are the commonest causes of death to workers in LA enforced premises.

Falling from a height is the most common cause of death to members of the public.

Other common causes are slipping, tripping or falling on the same level and drowning/asphyxiation.

TABLE 20:
Fatal injuries to employees (including trainees) and self-employed persons, 1986/87-1991/92

	1986/87	1987/88	1988/89	1989/90	1990/91	1991/92	Total 6 years
Total	19	18	20	31	20	30	138
By kind:							
Falls from a height	6	6	6	11	9	13	51
Struck by moving vehicle	7	5	6	9	3	5	35
Struck by moving object	1	2	2	4	2	4	15
Contact with moving machinery	2	-	4	1	4	3	14
Other kind	3	5	2	6	2	5	23
By industry activity:							
Hotel and catering	2	1	1	-	2	2	8
Social welfare	-	1	-	-	-	1	2
Retail	7	3	2	7	1	3	23
Wholesale	5	3	8	9	7	7	39
Office-based	1	1	2	1	1	3	9
Recreational*	1	-	-	-	2	5	8
Personal	-	-	-·	1	-	-	1
Other	3	9	7	13	7	9	48

* *Recreational premises were recently transferred to LA enforcement.*

57   Of the 144 fatal injuries to members of the public:

- 45 were concentrated in hotel and catering, 47 in social welfare, and 28 in retail distribution;

- age has been recorded for 118 cases, of which 15 were to children aged under 10, 72 were to people aged 60 or over.

58   The number of fatal injuries fluctuates from year to year, but from 1989/90 the number of fatalities to members of the public seems to be around 30 each year.   It must be borne in mind, however, that the figures are relatively small.

The number of deaths in each of the 6 years, 1986/87-1991/92 are displayed in Table 21 for kinds of accident and sectoral activity.

TABLE 21:
Fatal accidents to members of the public

| | Year | | | | | | Total |
	1986/87	1987/88	1988/89	1989/90	1990/91	1991/92	6 Years
Total	**14**	**19**	**14**	**30**	**35**	**32**	**144**
By Kind							
Fall from a height	6	8	6	10	17	11	58
Slip, trip, fall (same level)	2	2	1	5	5	6	21
Drowning/asphyxiation	3	5	2	4	3	5	22
Struck by a vehicle	-	-	2	3	4	5	14
Struck by an object	1	1	1	1	2	2	8
Contact with machinery	1	-	2	1	3	-	7
Other kind	1	3	-	6	1	3	14
By industry activity							
Hotel and catering	2	14	4	13	10	2	45
Social welfare	3	2	6	11	7	18	47
Retail	7	3	3	3	8	4	28
Office based	-	-	1	1	2	-	4
Recreational*	-	-	-	1	6	7	14
Other	2	-	-	1	2	1	6

* *Recreational premises were recently transferred to LA enforcement.*

59   64% of deaths to the public occurred in the hotel, catering and social welfare sectors.   Some of the seven public deaths in the recreational sector for 1991/92 may be in premises that are newly transferred to local authorities (under the EA Regulations).   During the last 3 years, the number of deaths to members of the public has been about 30 each year.

Accidents in the hotel and catering sector

60   This section of the report concentrates on accidents occurring in the hotel and catering sector and environments where food is handled. These sectors have particular kinds of accidents associated with them. Since 1986/87, the number of people employed in the hotel and catering sector has increased by about 20%. In 1991/92 there were 1.2 million people employed in this industry.

61   In 1991/92, 2984 injuries were reported. Of these, four were fatal, 871 were major and 2109 were over-3-day injuries. 83% of injuries were to employees (including trainees).

62   In the 6 year period, 1986/87-1991/92, the number of reported injuries was 12 734. Of these, there were 53 fatal injuries (most to members of the public), 3904 major injuries and 8777 over-3-day injuries. Just over four-fifths of injuries were to employees.

TABLE 22:
Injuries in the hotel and catering sector 1986/87-1991/92

Employment Status	Severity of Injury			
	Fatal	**Major**	**Over-3-day**	**Total**
Employee (including trainees)	7	1835	8762	10 604
Self-employed	1	18	15	34
Member of public	45	2051	†	2096
Total	**53**	**3904**	**8777**	**12 734**

† not reportable

This section goes on to examine injuries to employees and members of the public separately.

INJURIES TO EMPLOYEES (INCLUDING TRAINEES)

63   During the 6 years, 1986/87-1991/92, the hotel/catering industry reported 10 604 injuries to employees (including trainees). Of these:

- slips, trips and falls on the same level accounted for 35% of reported injuries -
    - of the slip and trip accidents, nearly two-fifths were as a result of lost footing or stepping out of a vehicle and landing awkwardly with a further two-fifths involving slipping on a slippery surface.
- Contact with harmful substance accounts for 16% of reported injuries -
    - most harmful substance injuries involve burns while using particular equipment. Commonest examples include fat fryers, griddles/toasters, convection ovens and boiling pans.
    - 11% of injuries were caused from burns from chemicals.
- 1720 (or 16%) of injuries resulted from handling, lifting or carrying. The bulk of these were from handling awkward or sharp objects (61%) with 32% from handling heavy objects.
- 1346 (or 13%) of injuries were caused from being struck by a moving, including flying or falling object. Just less than two-fifths of these were knife accidents, with a fifth struck by door, ramp etc. 14% were caused from being struck by part of fixtures/structures falling, with a further 14% caused by being struck by an object falling from table, shelf, stack.

Further details are given in Table 39 of Appendix Three.

64 Analysing industry activity in more detail:

■ just over a quarter of injuries occurred in premises where the main business was the hotel trade;

■ a further quarter of injuries to employees were in premises involved in mass production of food, ie canteens and messes;

■ 17% of injuries occurred in public houses and bars.

65 Not all injuries in the hotel and catering sector would involve the handling of food. The environment of accident has been examined. Just under half (or 4485) of all injuries to employees, in the hotel and catering sector occurred whilst preparing food (ie in kitchens and food preparation rooms). It should be noted that figures relate to 5 years of data, as environment of accident was not fully coded for 1986/87. A further 13% of accidents occurred in restaurants or bars with 8% on stairs/corridors/ entrances or exits.

INJURY TRENDS 1986/87-1991/92

66 The number of reported major and over-3-day injuries to employees have increased since 1986/87. The number of major injuries has almost doubled from 190 in 1986/87 to 374 in 1991/92. The number of over-3-day injuries has risen substantially to 2103 in 1991/92 (from 778 in 1986/87). The number of injuries in food preparation areas has almost doubled from 571 in 1987/88 to 1194 in 1991/92. To assess trends we must examine injury rates to take account of the changing numbers employed in the hotel and catering sector.

67 Tables 23 and 24 display trends in the rate of major and over-3-day categories of injury for the commonest kinds of accident in the hotel and catering sector. Over 70% of major injuries in this sector arise from slipping and tripping or falling on same level or from contact with harmful or hot substances. The major injury rate for these kinds rose substantially in the 4 years to 1989/90. The rise in rates for these kinds is the main reason why the rate of major injury in the hotel and catering sector is now 54% higher than 6 years ago. Also, there has been no improvement for other kinds of accident, including falling from a height.

TABLE 23:
Major injury rates for employees (including trainees) in the hotel and catering sector

Kind of accident	Injury rates per 100 000 employees					
	1986/87	1987/88	1988/89	1989/90	1990/91	1991/92
Slip, trip or fall on same level	11.9	14.3	16.7	19.5	19.0	20.4
Fall from a height	3.8	6.3	5.5	5.3	3.3	5.0
Contact with hot surfaces or harmful substances	1.7	2.6	2.3	3.0	3.3	3.6
Other kinds*	5.2	6.2	5.5	5.7	6.2	5.7
All kinds	**22.6**	**29.4**	**30.0**	**33.5**	**31.8**	**34.7**

* Other kinds include being struck by something fixed or stationary, contact with moving machinery, handling, lifting, carrying etc.
Injuries have been reported to HSE and LAs.

FIGURE O:
Over-3-day injury rates in the hotel and catering sector. Rates expressed per 100 000 employees

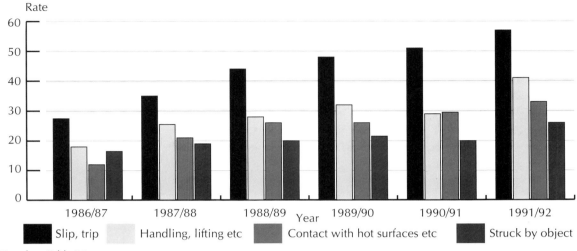

Based on Table 24.

68 Figure O displays the trends in the rate of over-3-day injury for the commonest kinds of accident. During the 6 years 1986/87-1991/92, the rate of injury has more than doubled for the three commonest kinds of over-3-day injury - slipping, tripping, falling (same level), handling, lifting, carrying and in contact with harmful substances. The rate of most kinds of injury rose in each year since 1986/87. As a result, the rate of over-3-day injury in the hotel and catering sector has more than doubled since then.

TABLE 24:
Over-3-day injury rates for employees (including trainees) in the hotel and catering sector.

Kind of accident	Injury rates per 100 000 employees					
	1986/87	1987/88	1988/89	1989/90	1990/91	1991/92
Slip, trip or fall on the same level	27.3	34.6	43.5	47.7	50.9	57.6
Handling, lifting, carrying	18.0	25.9	28.0	32.1	28.8	40.7
Contact with hot surfaces or harmful substances	12.4	21.5	26.2	26.0	29.1	32.4
Struck by an object	16.8	18.9	20.2	22.0	20.6	26.3
Other kinds*	21.1	24.5	29.3	31.1	30.4	37.1
All kinds	**95.6**	**125.4**	**147.2**	**158.9**	**159.8**	**194.1**

* *Other kinds include falls from a height, contact with machinery, struck by something stationary etc.*

Injuries have been reported to HSE and local authorities.

INJURIES TO MEMBERS OF THE PUBLIC IN HOTEL AND CATERING SECTOR

69 Fatal and major injuries to members of the public are reportable. Since 1986/87 employers and others of the LA sector have reported 2096 injuries, including 45 fatalities.

- Just over three-fifths of injuries (1295) were caused by slips, trips or falls on the same level. For those years where the agent of accident is available, 31% of slip, trip, fall (same level) injuries occurred while playing sports. 36% were from lost footing for no apparent reason/ stepping out of vehicle and landing awkwardly.

- Falls from a height accounted for 551 injuries to members of the public. Of these 35% were falls from sporting equipment and a further 35% involved falls off other equipment. Nearly a fifth of falls were down stairs.

- Just over three-fifths of injuries (or 988) occurred in holiday camp grounds. These figures are based on injuries occurring in 1988/89 onwards as this environment was identified then for the first time.

70   The number of major injuries has more than doubled from 211 in 1986/87 to 487 in 1991/92. The rise in reported major injuries stems mainly from increases in the numbers of slips, trips or falls (same level) - up from 121 to 317 - and increases in the numbers of falls from a height - up from 54 to 119.

Handling of food

71   This section concentrates on injuries occurring in environments where handling of food is most likely to take place ie kitchen, preparation room, canteen/restaurant, bakery, meat room. These environments are found in various industries and not just hotel and catering. They were fully recorded for years 1987/88 onwards. This section refers to injuries occurring in 1987/88-1991/92.

72   During the 5 year period 1987/88-1991/92, a total of 11 984 injuries were reported as being in 'handling of food' type environments. The bulk of injuries were to employees. There were two fatalities - both to members of the public. These occurred in canteen/restaurant environments.

INJURIES TO EMPLOYEES (INCLUDING TRAINEES)

73   In the 5 year period, there were 1470 major and 10 303 over-3-day injuries reported.
- Kitchens accounted for 54% of injuries to employees.
- Canteens/restaurants accounted for 18% of injuries.

74   The most common cause of accident was slip, trip, fall on the same level. 3840 or about a third of accidents were of this kind. Being struck by an object accounted for a further 20% (2301) of accidents. These were mainly knife accidents - 1582 in all. There were 2134 or 18% of injuries involving contact with hot surfaces or harmful substances.

75   Injuries took place mainly in two industries:
- retail distribution   5386 or 46%;
- hotels and catering   5106 or 43%.

76   Since 1987/88, the number of injuries occurring in 'handling of food' environments has increased by just over 50%. This is reflected in the increased number of injuries in the kitchen environment (rise of 87% from 1987/88).

Injuries occurring in retail distribution

77 This section of the report concentrates on injuries occurring in the retail distribution industries. Retail distribution includes such industries as: food retailing; dispensing and other chemists; retail distribution of clothing, footwear and leather goods, furnishing fabrics and household textiles; filling stations; retail distribution of books, stationery and office supplies and mixed retail businesses. In 1991/92 45% of injuries occurred in these industries.

78 The number of injuries reported to local authorities as occurring in retail distribution was 10 910 in 1991/92. Of those injuries:

- 10 172 (or 93%) were to employees, including two fatal, 933 major and 9237 over-3-day injuries;

- there were just 10 injuries to the self-employed including one fatal, two major and seven over-3-day injuries;

- members of the public with 728 total injuries (four fatal and 724 major) was 64% higher than the 444 reported in 1986/87.

INJURIES TO EMPLOYEES (INCLUDING TRAINEES)

79 Retail distribution is the largest employer in the services sector employing 2.3 million employees in 1991/92. It accounts for 46% of all injuries to employees. The numbers of fatal injuries are relatively small in number, with a total of 19 occurring in the 6 year period, 1986/87-1991/92.

Figures P and Q illustrate the kinds of major and over-3-day injury in the retail industry.

FIGURE P:
Major injuries to employees (including trainees) in retail distribution as reported to local authorities 1991/92

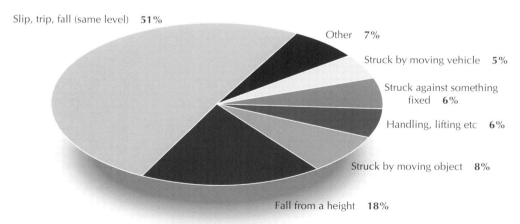

Percentages may not total 100% due to rounding.
Based on Table 41.

FIGURE Q:
Over-3-day injuries to employees (including trainees) in retail distribution as reported to local authorities 1991/92

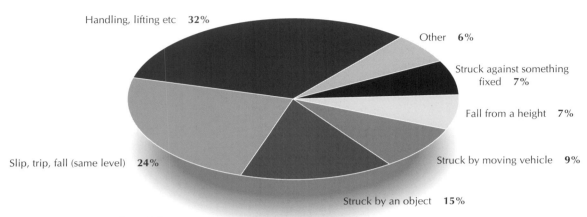

Handling, lifting etc **32%**

Other **6%**

Struck against something fixed **7%**

Fall from a height **7%**

Struck by moving vehicle **9%**

Struck by an object **15%**

Slip, trip, fall (same level) **24%**

Percentages may not total 100% due to rounding.
Based on Table 42.

80   Of reported major injuries in 1991/92:

■ just over half were from slips,trips,falls on the same level. Most of these were due to slips on slippery surfaces or tripping over obstructions;

■ 18% were due to falls from a height;

■ 8% were due to being struck by moving or flying objects (mainly falling from tables shelves and stacks);

■ well over 80% resulted in fractures predominantly to arms/wrists (about two-thirds) and legs/ankles (over a fifth).

Of over-3-day injuries:

■ 32% were due to handling, lifting or carrying and these mainly involved lifting awkward or heavy objects;

■ 24% involved slipping or tripping were mostly slipping on a slippery surface or lost footing;

■ 15% involved being struck by an object, mainly from non-powered vehicles, by objects falling from table or racks, or being struck by knives.

FATALITIES   · · · · · · · · · · ·

81   Of the 19 fatalities to employees in the 6 year period (1986/87-1991/92):

■ almost three-quarters involved being struck by a moving vehicle and falls from a height, with a further 11% attributed to slips, trips or falls on the same level;

■ seven involved either falling from or being struck by a fork lift truck;

■ eight of the fatalities were to employees under 26 and five were to employees aged 45-60. Only three fatalities were to women.

82   Tables 25 and 26 display trends in numbers and rates of major and over-3-day injury. For the period
        1986/87 to 1991/92, Figure R illustrates trends in all reported injuries.

FIGURE R:
*All injuries and incidence rates to employees (including trainees) in retail distribution as
reported to local authorities 1986/87-1991/92*

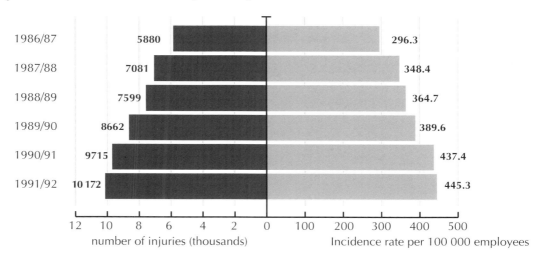

The number of reported injuries from the retail industry is over 10 000 and is 73% higher than 6 years
previously.

■   The rate of all reported injury has risen steadily in the last 6 years and the
    figure for 1991/92 is 50% higher than in 1986/87.

83   The number of reported major injuries has fluctuated throughout the 6 years varying from 814 in
        1986/87 to 1017 in 1990/91. During the 6 year period:

■   the rate of major injury has shown no real trend though the rate for 1991/92 is at the same
    level as in 1986/87;

■   the number of major injuries from slipping, tripping or falling on the same level rose
    substantially (up 40% to 476 in 1991/92), the number of contact with harmful substances
    more than doubled from 13 to 34;

■   there was a substantial fall in the number of major injuries due to being struck by an object;

■   in each of the 5 years, 1987/88-1991/92 over 20% of major injuries have occurred in either
    warehouses or sales areas.

84   For over-3-day injuries in retail distribution, as in services generally, there is an upward trend in the
        number of injuries reported. In the 6 year period:

■   the number of and rate of over-3-day injury has risen substantially. The rate is now 58%
    higher than in 1986/87;

■   during the 6 year period there have been substantial increases in the numbers of main kinds
    of over-3-day injury-

slipping, tripping	up 91% to 2177,
handling	up 117% to 2990,
contact with machinery	up 61% to 249,
struck by moving objects	up 44% to 1415;

- slips, trips, falls (same level) on an uneven surface more than doubled to 114 in 1991/92. Injuries resulting from slippery surfaces also rose by 79% from 399 to 713. They account for about a third of the reported over-3-day slip, trip, fall (same level) injuries. A further 32% can be attributed to 'lost footing' but the 1991/92 figure of 630 is only 2% higher than the 1987/88 figure of 616;

- struck by non-powered vehicles has the largest percentage increase, up from 36 in 1987/88 to 209 in 1991/92. Knife accidents rose from 295 to 364 or by 23% over the same period;

- back injuries feature prominently, with increases in sprains/strains - 991 in 1987/88 to 1402, (up 41%) in 1991/92 and bruises up 27% from 123 to 156. The largest increase in sprains/strains involved the arm/shoulder which rose 66% from 177 in 1987/88 to 294 in 1991/92 and bruises to legs increased by 36% from 175 to 238;

- when analysed by environment, the largest increase was seen in sales areas up 88%, from 1309 in 1987/88 to 2461 in 1991/92. Over the same period injuries in warehouses rose 54% (1689 to 2598) and loading bays up 37% (658 to 904).

85   The numbers of major and over-3-day injuries occurring by each kind of accident and in each workplace environment are given in full in Tables 40-42 of Appendix Three.

TABLE 25:
Injuries to employees (including trainees) occurring in retail distribution as reported to local authorities, 1986/87-1991/92

Severity of injury	1986/87	1987/88	1988/89	1989/90	1990/91	1991/92	Total 6 Years
Fatal	4	3	2	7	1	2	19
Major	814	971	935	952	1017	933	5622
Over-3-day	5062	6107	6662	7703	8697	9237	43 468
Total	**5880**	**7081**	**7599**	**8662**	**9715**	**10 172**	**49 109**

TABLE 26:
Incidence rates for injuries to employees (including trainees) in retail distribution as reported to HSE and local authorities, 1986/87-1991/92

Severity of injury	Incidence rate per 100 000 employees					
	1986/87	1987/88	1988/89	1989/90	1990/91	1991/92
Major	41.0	47.6	44.7	43.2	45.9	41.0
Over-3-day	255.1	300.6	319.8	346.1	391.4	404.1
Total*	**296.3**	**348.4**	**364.7**	**389.6**	**437.4**	**445.3**

* Includes fatal injuries

Reporting of injuries and the Labour Force Survey

86   The LFS has shown that only about a third of reportable non-fatal injuries to employees are actually being reported under RIDDOR, and that the situation is much worse for self-employed people who report only about one in twenty injuries.

87   The level of reporting by employers varies considerably between the main industry sectors, with about four-fifths of reportable non-fatal injuries being reported in the energy sector, about two-fifths in manufacturing and construction, a fifth in agriculture and a quarter in the services sector. Within the large and diverse services sector reporting levels vary with about one in four in health and in personal services, one in six in distribution and hotels, one in ten in social, welfare and recreational services, and less than one in ten in business services.

88   Local authorities receive only around one in seven reports on injuries to employees. As a result, the real risk of reportable injury in industries enforced by local authorities is therefore substantially higher than reported injuries suggest. In the LA sector the rate of injury reportable under RIDDOR as estimated from the LFS, is highest in the social and recreational services and in distribution which is consistent with rates based on injuries actually reported under RIDDOR.

HOURS OF WORK AND PART-TIME WORKING

89   Rates of reported injury in the services sector are understated not just because reporting levels are relatively low, but also because of the extent of part-time working in the services sector. For example, less than 10% of employees in manufacturing work fewer than 30 hours a week (the standard Employment Department definition of a part-time worker). The figure for the services sector is over 25%. As a result, the average weekly hours of work per employee is less in the services sector (at around 35 hours) than in manufacturing (over 41 hours). Standard rates of injury expressed per capita conceal the relative extent of part-time working in the services sector.

90   We can express rates of injury in terms of **full-time employee equivalent** to working the national average of just over 37 hours per week. The figures on hours of work are from the Labour Force Survey, the only comprehensive source of information on hours.

91   The effect of expressing rates of injury per full-time equivalent employee is to place services and other main sectors on the same level in terms of average exposure to work. Rates of many service sector industries are adjusted upwards relative to those in manufacturing. For some industries of the manufacturing and service sectors, Table 27 displays both standard per capita rate and rates per full-time equivalent (FTE) employees from the LFS. The rate of industries in the LA sector is increased by around 14-18% but those of manufacturing are decreased by about 10%.

92   The effect of expressing rates per full-time equivalent employees is to substantially reduce the gap in injury performance of parts of manufacturing and service sectors. The LFS suggests that:

■   working in retail, wholesale and hotel and catering industries has over four-fifths of the risk of part of manufacturing;

■   working in social welfare and recreational services has at least the same risk as in part of manufacturing.

TABLE 27 :
Rates of reportable injury from HSE Supplement to the 1990 Labour Force Survey

Industry	Rate per 100 000 Employed people	Full-time equivalent (a)
Manufacturing		
- Extraction of coal, minerals, ores	8010	6770
- Food, drink and tobacco	5090	4600
- Other manufacturing	3110	2810
Services		
- Social welfare and recreational*	3110	3630
- Health services	2970	3360
- Retail, wholesale, hotel and catering	2120	2420
- Personal services*	1330	1450
All industries	**2630**	**2630**

* *Social welfare, recreational and personal services are part of the consumer/personal industry (see paragraph 45).*

(a) *Expressed in terms of a standard employee working the national average hours of work (37).*

PART-TIME EMPLOYEES

93   Over $4\frac{1}{2}$ million employees work less than 30 hours a week in Great Britain. The bulk of these, 4 million, are employed in service sector industries but around $1\frac{2}{3}$ million are employed in the distribution (retail and wholesale) and hotel and catering industries - the largest concentration of part time working.

94   The accident questions on the 1990 LFS allow rates of workplace injury in part-time employees to be determined for the first time. Furthermore, rates per full-time equivalent employee can be derived using estimates of average hours worked by part-time and other employees. For example, in the distribution and hotel and catering sectors combined, the weekly hours of part-time employees is about 15 hours on average per employee. For employees working more than 30 hours, the average weekly hours is almost three times higher at 44 hours per employee. Such differences in average exposure to work are standardised in rates of injury expressed per full-time equivalent employee.

95   For the distribution and hotel and catering industry sector, Figure S displays rates of injury, on both standard per capita and full-time equivalent bases. The rate per FTE is higher in part-time employees than other employees; and not just for distribution but also for other industries where part-time employees are employed.

Expressed per full-time equivalent employee,

■   the risk of injury to part-time staff is higher than for staff working fuller hours.

96   The risk of injury to workers reflects not just the industry of their employer but the nature of their jobs or occupations. The higher rate of injury in part-time staff could plausibly be linked to their jobs. For example, fewer part-time employees are employed in the lowest risk managerial, clerical and administrative occupations.

FIGURE S:
Rates of injuries for part-time and full-time employees - retail, wholesale, hotel and catering industries

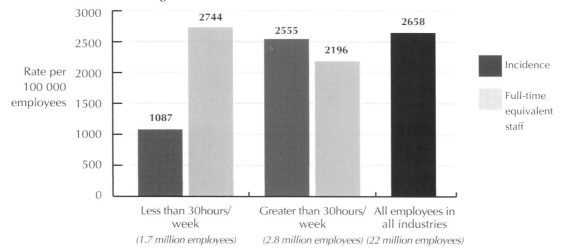

FIGURE T:
Rates of injuries for part-time and full-time employees - retail and hotel and catering industries

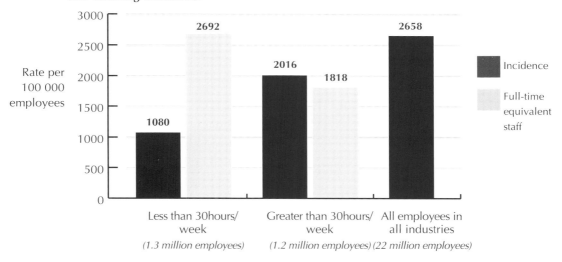

97   From the LFS we can compare rates of injury for part-time and full-time employees within the main occupational groups that are to be found in the distribution and hotel and catering industries. For the retail and hotel and catering group of jobs, Figure T displays the rate of reportable injury on both standard per capita and full-time equivalent bases. The rate per FTE is substantially higher in part-time employees.

This result is based on part-time and full-time people doing a similar range of retail and wholesale jobs, excluding lower risk managerial and clerical staff. Further dissaggregation shows that more full-time than part-time employees are in individual retail and hotel and catering jobs of relatively high risk. Occupation appears not to explain the higher rate of injury in part-time employees. The LFS also suggests that for retail and catering jobs, the rate of less serious (non-reportable) injury is also higher in part-time employees.

Expressed per full-time equivalent employee:

■   the risk of injury to part-time employees in retail and hotel and catering jobs is about 50% higher than in full-time employees.

APPENDICES

APPENDIX ONE:

Sources of local authority HSW statistics and employment statistics

1   Each year local authorities are requested to complete a health and safety return (LAE 1 form). For 1991/92, LAE 1 forms were received from 404 LAs (88% of the 461 LAs with HSW enforcement responsibility). The LAE 1 forms are the sole source of information about premises, visits, complaints, staff resources and enforcement activity. Full LAE 1 statistics are given in Tables 43-50.

2   The figures derived from the LAE 1 returns are estimates for the LA sector throughout Great Britain (unless otherwise stated). This national picture is obtained by grossing up data from the 404 LAE 1 forms received to give estimates for the total of 461 authorities.

3   The second source of LA statistics is the LA RIDDOR database of injuries reported by employers. This is maintained by the Local Authority Unit (LAU). Since the introduction of RIDDOR in 1986, LAs have sent copies of individual RIDDOR injury report forms to the LAU. The LA RIDDOR database was primarily established for operational purposes. However, it has proved to be a rich and reliable source of statistics on injuries to employed persons and members of the public in the LA sector and is now the sole source of LA injury statistics used throughout this report. Consequently only a small amount of information on injuries is sought on the 1991/92 LAE 1 form.

4   The source of employment figures is the Employment Department, which breaks down the figures by industry activity according to the Standard Industrial Classification 1980 (SIC). However, the employment figures do not distinguish between enforcing authorities, LA or HSE, for any activity. Incidence rates are therefore based on employee injury reports copied by LAs and some injuries reported to HSE.

APPENDIX TWO:

Definition of the industries used to analyse the LA RIDDOR database

1   Injuries recorded on the LA RIDDOR database are classified according to the Standard Industrial Classification 1980 (SIC). The SIC is widely used throughout Government, particularly for the production of employment statistics by industry. Use of the SIC for local authority injury statistics allows the calculation of injury rates for the main LA enforced industries.

2   The definitions used in the SIC are slightly different from the traditional LAE 1 'type of premises', and take no account of enforcing authority boundaries. This is why it is necessary to include those injuries reported to HSE when calculating injury rates.

3   The main LA enforced industries are:

Retail: Retail distribution (SIC Class 64/65)

Wholesale: Wholesale distribution (including dealing with scrap and waste materials): Miscellaneous transport services and storage (SIC Classes 61, 62, 77)

Hotel and Catering: Hotels and catering (SIC Class 66)

Offices: Commission agents, banking and finance; insurance; business services (SIC Classes 63, 81, 82, 83).

4   The industries where premises transferred to LAs under the Health and Safety (Enforcing Authority) Regulations 1989 are mainly concentrated in:

Social welfare, professional organisations, religious bodies and other community services (SIC Class 96).

Recreational, sporting and cultural services (SIC Class 97)

Personal services (SIC Class 98)

These make up consumer/personal services (SIC Classes 96, 97, 98)

APPENDIX THREE:

Tables of detailed statistics

Tables 1-27 in are in the main text of Part 3 of the report

Table   Title

1   Summary of LA health and safety statistics for Great Britain.

2   Premises enforced by local authorities 1991/92, and changes since 1986/87 and 1990/91.

3   Changes in LA staff resources since 1986/87.

4   Changes in visits made by type of visit since 1990/91.

5   Changes in visits by type of premises.

6   Changes in visits made per 100 premises, since 1986/87.

7   Changes in formal notices issued 1986/87-1991/92.

8   Prosecution cases completed.

9   Conviction rates by type of legislation.

10   Employment status and severity of injury 1991/92.

11   Injury trends for first 6 years of RIDDOR: injuries to employees (including trainees), self-employed and members of the public.

12   Injury trends per full-time equivalent staff, 1986/87-1991/92.

13   Kind of accident and severity of injury 1991/92. Employees (including trainees).

14   Kind of accident and industry, injuries to employees (including trainees) reported to LAs, 1991/92.

15   Environment of accident and severity of injury, injuries to employees (including trainees) as reported to LAs, 1991/92.

16   Injury trends by activity 1986/87-1991/92. Injuries to employees (including trainees).

17   Major injury rates for employees (including trainees).

18   Over-3-day injury rates for employees (including trainees).

19   Fatal accidents 1986/87-1991/92. Kind by employment status.

20   Fatal injuries to employees (including trainees) and self-employed persons, 1986/87-1991/92.

21   Fatal accidents to members of the public.

22   Injuries in the hotel and catering sector 1986/87-1991/92.

23   Major injury rates for employees in the hotel and catering sector.

24   Over-3-day injury rates for employees (including trainees) in hotel and catering.

25   Injuries to employees (including trainees) occurring in retail distribution as reported to LAs, 1986/87-1991/92.

26   Incidence rates for injuries to employees (including trainees) in retail distribution as reported to HSE and LAs, 1986/87-1991/92.

27   Rates of reportable injury from HSE Supplement to the 1990 Labour Force Survey.

28   Kind of accident and severity of injury 1991/92.

29   Kind of accident and industry activity 1991/92.

30   Environment of accident and severity of injury 1991/92.

31   Major injury incidence rates for employees by activity 1991/92.

TABLE 28:
Kind of accident and severity of injury 1991/92 (employees, self-employed and members of the public)

Kind of accident	Fatal	Severity of injury Major	Over-3-day	Total
Slip, trip, fall (same level)	6	2425(56%)	4714(24%)	7145(30%)
Handling, lifting, carrying	1	149(3%)	6483(33%)	6633(27%)
Struck by a moving object	6	219(5%)	2712(14%)	2937(12%)
Fall from a height	24	884(20%)	1632(8%)	2540(10%)
Struck by a moving vehicle	10	162(4%)	1458(7%)	1630(7%)
Struck against something fixed	1	114(3%)	1207(6%)	1322(5%)
Hot surfaces and harmful substances	1	122(3%)	640(3%)	763(3%)
Contact with moving machinery	3	95(2%)	501(3%)	599(2%)
Drowning or asphyxiation	6	4	14	24
Other	4	157(4%)	451(2%)	612(3%)
Total	**62**	**4331**	**19 812**	**24 205**

Percentages are shown in brackets and may not total 100% due to rounding.

TABLE 29:
Kind of accident and industry activity 1991/92: (employees, self-employed and members of the public)

Kind of accident	Retail	Activity Wholesale	Hotel and catering	Office based
Slip, trip, fall (same level)	3211	388	1167	386
Handling, lifting, carrying	3047	585	456	305
Struck by a moving object	1515	283	314	144
Fall from a height	862	263	326	205
Struck by a moving vehicle	880	252	38	24
Struck against something fixed	699	100	111	65
Hot surfaces and harmful substances	217	20	401	20
Contact with moving machinery	291	78	67	29
Other	188	24	104	32
Total	**10 910**	**1993**	**2984**	**1210**

TABLE 30:
Environment of accident and severity of injury, 1991/92 (employees, self-employed and members of the public)

Environment of accident	Fatal	Severity of injury Major	Over-3-day	Total
Warehouse, storage	6	360	4265	4631
Sales areas	3	717	2629	3349
Off the premises (eg delivery)	5	310	2402	2717
Loading bays	3	241	2378	2622
Food preparation areas, kitchens	-	216	1600	1816
Stairs, corridors, entrances, exits	2	398	1031	1431
Offices	1	191	1047	1239
Residential areas	18	377	296	691
Post office sorting room	-	24	652	676
Restaurants, bars	-	151	514	665
Car parks	2	150	212	364
Staff room	-	88	236	324
Holiday camp grounds	1	295	13	309
Meat room	-	17	276	293
Cellar	1	13	269	283
Mail order	-	5	268	273
Cold room	-	25	231	256
Bakery	-	34	200	234
Sporting activity	11	141	74	226
Leisure/recreation	2	170	48	220
Other	7*	408	1171	1586
Total	**62**	**4331**	**19 812**	**24 205**

* Includes 1 fatal injury in workshop/machine room, 1 in cold stores and 5 in other environments.

TABLE 31:

Major injury incidence rates for employees (including trainees) by activity 1991/92

Activity	Major injuries reported to LAs (LAU)	Major injuries reported to LAs and HSE*	Injury incidence rate per 100 000 employees *
Retail	933	951	41.0
Wholesale	236	501	46.1
Hotel and catering	374	406	34.7
Office based	188	214	9.1
Total Consumer/personal services	134	616	38.8
of which:			
Social welfare	48	286	31.8
Recreational	79	278	55.7
Personal services	7	52	27.6

* Injury incidence rates are based on injuries reported to LAs and HSE.

TABLE 32:

Over-3-day injury incidence rates for employees (including trainees) by activity 1991/92

Activity	Over-3-day injuries reported to LAs (LAU)	Over-3-day injuries reported to LAs and HSE *	Injury incidence rate per 100 000 employees *
Retail	9237	9368	404.1
Wholesale	1731	3285	302.4
Hotel and catering	2103	2274	194.1
Office based	952	1189	50.5
Total Consumer/personal services	504	4517	284.4
of which:			
Social welfare	224	2733	303.6
Recreational	228	1384	277.1
Personal services	52	400	212.4

* Injury incidence rates are based on injuries reported to LAs and HSE.

TABLE 33:

All injuries reported to local authorities 1991/92

STANDARD INDUSTRIAL CLASSIFICATION	EMPLOYEES (INC. TRAINEES)			
	Fatal	Major	Over-3-day	Total
0 AGRICULTURE, FORESTRY AND FISHING	-	1	6	7
01 Agriculture and horticulture	-	-	6	6
02 Forestry	-	-	-	-
03 Fishing	-	1	-	1
1 ENERGY AND WATER SUPPLY INDUSTRIES	-	14	143	157
11 Coal extraction and manufacture of solid fuels	-	-	1	1
12 Coke ovens	-	-	-	-
13 Extraction of mineral oil and natural gas	-	-	-	-
14 Mineral oil processing	-	-	-	-
15 Nuclear fuel production	-	-	-	-
16 Production and distribution of electricity, gas and other forms of energy	-	13	133	146
17 Water supply industry	-	1	9	10
2 EXTRACTION OF MINERALS, ORES, MANUFACTURE OF MINERALS AND CHEMICALS	-	4	33	37
21/23 Extraction and preparation of metalliferous ores and minerals nes	-	-	-	-
22 Metal manufacturing	-	-	-	-
24 Manufacture of non-metallic mineral products	-	1	6	7
25 Chemical industry	-	3	27	30
26 Production of man-made fibres	-	-	-	-
3 METAL GOODS, ENGINEERING AND VEHICLES INDUSTRIES	2	42	260	304
31 Manufacture of metal goods not elsewhere specified	-	-	5	5
32 Mechanical engineering	1	13	96	110
33 Manufacture of office machinery and data processing equipment	1	10	41	52
34 Electrical and electronic engineering	-	13	52	65
35 Manufacture of motor vehicles and parts thereof	-	4	52	56
36 Manufacture of other transport equipment	-	1	1	2
37 Instrument engineering	-	1	13	14
4 OTHER MANUFACTURING INDUSTRIES	-	43	743	786
41/42 Food, drink and tobacco manufacturing industries	-	29	666	695
43 Textile industry	-	-	2	2
44 Manufacture of leather or leather goods	-	-	-	-
45 Footwear and clothing industries	-	1	2	3
46 Timber and wooden furniture industries	-	2	11	13
47 Manufacture of paper and paper products, printing and publishing	-	5	41	46
48 Processing of rubber and plastics	-	5	16	21
49 Other manufacturing industries	-	1	5	6
2-4 TOTAL MANUFACTURING	2	89	1036	1127
5 CONSTRUCTION	1	62	146	209
6 DISTRIBUTION, HOTELS AND CATERING; REPAIRS	10	1531	12920	14461
61/62 Wholesale distribution (inc. dealing in scrap and waste materials)	6	208	1438	1652
63 Commission agents	-	-	1	1
64/65 Retail distribution	2	933	9237	10172
66 Hotels and catering	2	374	2103	2479
67 Repair of consumer goods and vehicles	-	16	141	157
7 TRANSPORT AND COMMUNICATION	3	242	3677	3922
71 Railways	-	-	-	-
72 Other inland transport	2	104	1267	1373
74 Sea transport	-	-	5	5
75 Air transport	-	1	17	18
76 Supporting services to transport	-	6	79	85
77 Miscellaneous transport services and storage nes	1	28	293	322
79 Postal services and telecommunications	-	103	2016	2119
8 BANKING, FINANCE, INSURANCE, BUSINESS SERVICES AND LEASING	4	207	1035	1246
81 Banking and finance	1	73	481	555
82 Insurance, except for compulsory social security	-	18	102	120
83 Business services	2	97	368	467
84 Renting of moveables	1	13	54	68
85 Owning and dealing in real estate	-	6	30	36
9 OTHER SERVICES	5	222	769	996
91/92 Public admin, national defence, compulsory social security, sanitary	1	80	228	309
93 Education	-	6	15	21
94 Research and development	-	-	8	8
95 Medical and other health services, including veterinary services	-	2	14	16
96 Other services provided to the general public	1	48	224	273
97 Recreational services and other cultural services	3	79	228	310
98 Personal services	-	7	52	59
99 Domestic services	-	-	-	-
6-9 TOTAL SERVICE INDUSTRIES	22	2202	18401	20625
UNCLASSIFIED	-	-	-	-
ALL INDUSTRIES	25	2368	19732	22125

TABLE 33   cont...

| | SELF EMPLOYED | | | | MEMBERS OF PUBLIC | | | |
	Fatal	Major	Over-3-day	Total	Fatal	Major	Over-3-day	Total
0	-	1	-	1	-	1	"	1
01	-	1	-	1	-	1	"	1
02	-	-	-	-	-	-	"	-
03	-	-	-	-	-	-	"	-
1	-	-	-	-	-	3	"	3
11	-	-	-	-	-	-	"	-
12	-	-	-	-	-	-	"	-
13	-	-	-	-	-	-	"	-
14	-	-	-	-	-	-	"	-
15	-	-	-	-	-	-	"	-
16	-	-	-	-	-	3	"	3
17	-	-	-	-	-	-		
2	-	-	-	-	-	-	"	-
21/23	-	-	-	-	-	-	"	-
22	-	-	-	-	-	-	"	-
24	-	-	-	-	-	-	"	-
25	-	-	-	-	-	-	"	-
26	-	-	-	-	-	-	"	-
3	1	5	-	6	-	-	"	-
31	-	-	-	-	-	-	"	-
32	1	2	-	3	-	-	"	-
33	-	1	-	1	-	-	"	-
34	-	-	-	-	-	-	"	-
35	-	1	-	1	-	-	"	-
36	-	-	-	-	-	-	"	-
37								
4	1	2	-	3	-	1	"	1
41/42	-	-	-	-	-	-	"	-
43	-	-	-	-	-	-	"	-
44	-	-	-	-	-	-	"	-
45	-	-	-	-	-	-	"	-
46	1	1	-	2	-	-	"	-
47	-	-	-	-	-	1	"	1
48	-	1	-	1	-	-	"	-
49	-	-	-	-	-	1	"	1
2-4	2	7	-	9	-	1	"	1
5	-	8	13	21	-	1	"	1
6	1	12	17	30	6	1223	"	1229
61/62	-	-	3	3	-	11	"	11
63	-	2	7	10	-	-	"	-
64/65	1	2	7	10	4	724	"	728
66	-	10	6	16	2	487	"	489
67	-	-	1	1	-	1	"	1
7	-	3	10	13	-	23	"	23
71	-	1	6	7	-	2	"	2
72	-	-	-	-	-	-	"	-
74	-	-	-	-	-	-	"	-
75	-	-	-	-	-	20	"	20
76	-	2	3	5	-	-	"	-
77	-	-	1	1	-	1	"	1
79								
8	-	3	3	6	-	63	"	1
81	-	1	-	1	-	13	"	13
82	-	-	-	-	-	-	"	-
83	-	2	3	5	-	48	"	48
84	-	-	-	-	-	-	"	-
85	-	-	-	-	-	2	"	2
9	2	26	37	65	26	588	"	614
91/92	-	3	2	5	-	1	"	1
93	-	-	-	-	-	-	"	-
94	-	-	-	-	-	-	"	-
95	-	-	-	-	-	4	"	4
96	-	-	-	-	18	321	"	339
97	2	23	35	60	7	262	"	269
98	-	-	-	-	1	-	"	1
99	-	-	-	-	-	-	"	-
6-9	3	44	67	114	32	1897	"	1929
	5	60	80	145	32	1903	"	193

TABLE 34:
Incidence rates for injuries to employees (including trainees)* 1991/92

Standard industrial classificsation 1990	Incidence rates per 100 000 employees			
	Fatal	Major	Over-3-day	Total
0 Agriculture, forestry and fishing	**6.7**	**150.0**	**527.8**	**684.5**
01 Agriculture and horticulture	5.9	149.9	478.6	634.4
02 Forestry	38.5	269.2	2346.2	2653.8
03 Fishing	"	"	"	"
1 Energy and water supply industries	**0.0**	**500.0**	**7166.7**	**7666.7**
11 Coal extraction and manufacture of solid fuels	1.3	10.6	74.5	86.4
12 Coke ovens	0.0	428.6	6142.9	6571.4
13 Extraction of mineral oil and natural gas	0.0	8.0	38.1	46.1
14 Mineral oil processing	5.7	108.0	869.3	983.0
15 Nuclear fuel production	0.0	53.7	1228.2	1281.9
16 Production and distribution of electricity, gas and other forms of energy	1.9	111.3	1527.4	1640.6
17 Water supply industry	0.0	126.4	1659.0	1785.4
2 Extraction of minerals, ores, manufacture of minerals and chemicals	**3.0**	**159.5**	**1345.8**	**1508.4**
21/23 Extraction and preparation of metalliferous ores and minerals nes	0.0	7.4	92.6	100.0
22 Metal manufacturing	6.7	215.9	1882.8	2105.3
24 Manufacture of non-metallic mineral products	4.8	206.8	1659.7	1871.3
25 Chemical industry	0.3	123.2	1047.1	1170.7
26 Production of man-made fibres	16.1	96.8	1258.1	1371.0
3 Metal goods, engineering and vehicles industries	**1.3**	**109.5**	**907.8**	**1018.6**
31 Manufacture of metal goods not elsewhere specified	1.1	220.0	1467.0	1688.1
32 Mechanical engineering	2.2	104.7	715.7	822.6
33 Manufacture of office machinery and data processing equipment	2.8	39.2	291.3	333.3
34 Electrical and electronic engineering	0.4	63.5	586.8	650.7
35 Manufacture of motor vehicles and parts thereof	0.4	114.3	1659.4	1774.1
36 Manufacture of other transport equipment	1.9	136.1	1198.8	1336.8
37 Instrument engineering	0.0	37.4	297.8	335.2
4 Other manufacturing industries	**0.9**	**133.6**	**1322.9**	**1457.5**
41/42 Food, drink and tobacco manufacturing industries	1.2	203.4	2596.8	2801.4
43 Textile industry	0.6	114.7	956.9	1072.2
44 Manufacture of leather or leather goods	0.0	80.7	708.1	788.8
45 Footwear and clothing industries	0.0	37.8	323.0	360.7
46 Timber and wooden furniture industries	0.5	189.6	1103.1	1293.3
47 Manufacture of paper and paper products, printing and publishing	0.9	79.0	716.8	796.7
48 Processing of rubber and plastics	1.5	176.5	1459.5	1637.5
49 Other manufacturing industries	2.9	59.4	469.6	531.9
2-4 Total manufacturing	**1.4**	**126.4**	**1139.8**	**1267.6**
5 Construction	**8.8**	**272.4**	**1588.0**	**1869.2**
6 Distribution, hotels and catering; repairs	**0.4**	**45.9**	**362.1**	**408.4**
61/62 Wholesale distribution (inc. dealing in scrap and waste materials)	1.3	43.9	275.4	320.6
63 Commission agents	0.0	0.0	30.3	30.3
64/65 Retail distribution	0.1	41.0	404.1	445.3
66 Hotels and catering	0.3	34.7	194.1	229.0
67 Repair of consumer goods and vehicles	0.5	192.1	1349.6	1542.3
7 Transport and communication	**2.0**	**73.0**	**925.4**	**1000.4**
71 Railways	0.0	0.0	0.0	0.0
72 Other inland transport	4.5	79.5	772.3	856.3
74 Sea transport	3.1	6.2	80.7	90.1
75 Air transport	0.0	51.9	722.9	774.9
76 Supporting services to transport	5.4	167.1	1400.8	1573.4
77 Miscellaneous transport services and storage nes	1.6	56.9	431.2	489.6
79 Postal services and telecommunications	0.0	89.3	1594.9	1684.2
8 Banking, finance, insurance, business services and leasing	**0.3**	**11.1**	**60.6**	**72.0**
81 Banking and finance	0.2	12.1	80.4	92.7
82 Insurance, except for compulsory social security	0.0	6.7	38.5	45.2
83 Business services	0.4	8.5	40.8	49.7
84 Renting of moveables	1.6	42.8	187.5	231.9
85 Owning and dealing in real estate	0.0	13.6	105.5	119.1
9 Other services	**0.4**	**58.3**	**591.1**	**649.7**
91/92 Public admin, national defence, compulsory social security, sanitory	0.7	83.7	1130.1	1214.5
93 Education	0.1	62.5	275.4	337.9
94 Research and development	0.0	60.6	415.7	476.3
95 Medical and other health services, including veterinary services	0.1	42.5	639.0	681.6
96 Other services provided to the general public	0.3	31.8	303.6	335.7
97 Recreational services and other cultural services	1.0	55.7	277.1	333.7
98 Personal services	0.0	27.6	212.4	240.0
99 Domestic services	0.0	0.0	0.0	0.0
6-9 Total services industries	**0.5**	**47.8**	**461.2**	**509.5**
Unclassified	"	"	"	"
All industries	**1.2**	**77.1**	**671.7**	**750.0**

*Injuries reported mainly to LAs and some to HSE for parts of the services sector; and mainly to HSE and a few to LA's for other industries

TABLE 35:

Non-fatal injuries to employees (including trainees) as reported to local authorities, 1986/87-1991/92

Kind of accident	Number of non-fatal injuries					
	1986/87	1987/88	1988/89	1989/90	1990/91	1991/92
Injured while handling, lifting or carrying	3459	4165	4741	5682	6269	6607
Slip, trip or fall on same level	3600	4132	4696	5683	6311	5785
Struck by moving inc. flying/falling object	2154	2075	2312	2601	2734	2872
Falls from a height	1488	1750	1923	2085	2084	2122
Struck by moving vehicle	863	1222	1280	1546	1512	1569
Struck against something fixed or stationary	1043	1006	1014	1203	1331	1295
Exposure to or contact with harmful substance	323	497	531	583	704	750
Contact with moving machinery or material	324	450	517	567	588	559
Contact with electricity or an electrical discharge	56	49	65	79	61	132
Injured by an animal	104	138	138	228	197	102
Exposure to an explosion	20	25	17	17	20	34
Exposure to fire	8	18	11	13	13	18
Drowning or asphyxiation	3	1	-	1	1	16
Other kind of accident	63	140	71	106	149	239
Kind undetermined	7	-	-	-	-	-
Total	**13515**	**15668**	**17316**	**20394**	**21974**	**22100**

TABLE 36:
Injuries to employees (including trainees) as reported to local authorities 1991/92

Kind of accident	Retail distribution	Wholesale distribution (a)	Hotels and Catering	Offices (b)
Injured while handling, lifting or carrying	3045	581	450	304
Slip, trip or fall on same level	2653	381	844	342
Struck by moving inc. flying/falling object	1485	280	303	142
Struck by moving vehicle	854	250	35	23
Falls from a height	795	260	205	189
Struck against something fixed or stationary	691	100	102	65
Contact with moving machinery or material	264	78	67	27
Exposure to or contact with harmful substance	214	20	399	20
Contact with electricity or an electrical discharge	44	3	25	9
Exposure to an explosion	13	2	13	1
Injured by an animal	10	3	1	2
Drowning or asphyxiation	4	-	8	1
Exposure to fire	4	-	5	-
Other kind of accident	96	16	22	18
Total	**10172**	**1974**	**2479**	**1143**

(a) Includes dealing in scrap and waste materials: Miscellaneous transport services and storage.

(b) Includes commission agents, banking and finance; insurance; business services.

TABLE 37:

Injuries to employees (including trainees) as reported to local authorities 1991/92

Kind of accident	Social welfare (a)	Recreational (b)	Personal services	Total Consumer/ personal services
Slip, trip or fall on same level	84	83	15	182
Injured while handling, lifting or carrying	97	50	21	168
Falls from a height	24	82	5	111
Struck by moving inc. flying/falling object	18	32	1	51
Exposure to or contact with harmful substance	8	17	4	29
Contact with moving machinery or material	11	7	1	19
Injured by an animal	1	16	2	19
Struck against something fixed or stationary	11	3	3	17
Struck by moving vehicle	-	8	4	12
Contact with electricity or electrical discharge	2	5	2	9
Drowning or asphyxiation	-	1	-	1
Exposure to fire	1	-	-	1
Exposure to an explosion	1	-	-	1
Other kind of accident	15	6	1	22
Total	**273**	**310**	**59**	**642**

(a) Includes social welfare, charitable and community services; trade unions, business and professional associations; religious organisations and similar assoications; tourist offices and other community services.

(b) Includes recreational and other cultural services.

TABLE 38:

Injuries to employees (including trainees) as reported to local authorities 1991/92

Environment	Fatal	Severity of injuriy Major	Over-3-day	Total
Warehouse/storage	5	357	4256	4618
Sales areas	-	288	2628	2916
Off premises - On delivery	4	291	2387	2682
Loading bays	3	226	2369	2598
Food preparation/kitchen	-	209	1599	1808
Offices	1	179	1047	1227
Stairs, corridors, entrances/exits etc	1	178	1030	1209
Post office - sorting room	-	24	652	676
Bars/restaurants	-	105	513	618
Residential areas	1	49	295	345
Staff room	-	62	236	298
Meat room	-	16	275	291
Cellar	-	13	269	282
Mail order	-	5	268	273
Car parks	-	50	212	262
Cold room	-	25	231	256
Bakery	-	34	200	234
Leisure/recreation	1	17	46	64

Other environments

Environment	Fatal	Major	Over-3-day	Total
Vehicle repair	-	10	102	112
Workshop/machine room	1	27	82	110
Tyre and exhaust	-	8	77	85
Sporting activities	2	33	40	75
Airport terminal	-	1	58	59
Milk depot	-	6	49	55
Battery charging	-	4	49	53
Plant room/boiler room	-	5	45	50
Post office - counter	-	2	33	35
Holiday camp grounds	-	13	13	26
Print room	-	4	21	25
Cold store	1	2	20	23
Laundry room	-	2	11	13
Construction - other	-	4	5	9
Golf courses	-	2	7	9
Undertakers	-	1	6	7
Construction - retail	-	-	5	5
Accommodation of animals	-	1	3	4
Playground	-	2	-	2
Launderette	-	1	1	2
Agricultural fairs	-	-	1	1
Other environments	5	112	591	708
Total	**25**	**2368**	**19 732**	**22 125**

TABLE 39:

Main kinds of accident : injuries to employees (including trainees) in hotel and catering sector 1986/87-1991/92

Kind/Agent of Accident	Total Number of Injuries
Contact with harmful substance of which:	1737 (a)
Fat fryer	267
Griddles	225
Chemical burns	199
Convection top	78
Boiling pans	55
Water boilers	39
Steaming ovens	33
Gas/dust/fumes	20
Slip, trip or fall on same level of which:	3671
Slippery surface	1420
Stepping out of vehicle	1415
Obstruction	360
On stairs	231
Uneven surface	200
Handling, lifting or carrying of which:	1720
Awkward/sharp objects	1051
Heavy objects	553

(a) Agent breakdown for 5 year period only (1987/88-1991/92).

TABLE 40:

Injuries to employees (including trainees) occurring in retail distribution as reported to local authorities 1987/88-1991/92(a)

Environment	1987/88				1988/89			
	Fatal	Major	Over-3-day	Total	Fatal	Major	Over-3-day	Total
Wharehouse/Storage	2	228	1689	1919	-	205	1887	2092
Sales areas	-	236	1309	1545	-	246	1588	1834
Loading bays	1	92	658	751	1	85	696	782
Stairs, corridors, entrances/exits etc	*	*	*	*	1	110	432	543
Food preparation/kitchen	-	31	228	259	-	49	255	304
Off premises - on delivery	-	54	477	531	-	77	463	540
Meat room	-	24	243	267	-	35	270	305
Mail order	*	*	*	*	-	1	168	169
Cold room	*	*	*	*	-	10	103	113
Bars/restaurants	-	27	166	193	-	22	176	198
Bakery	-	19	135	154	-	34	173	207
Offices	-	22	73	95	-	9	126	135
Staff room	*	*	*	*	-	16	49	65
Car parks	*	*	*	*	-	16	62	78
Other environments	-	238	1129	1367	-	20	214	234
Total	**3**	**971**	**6107**	**7081**	**2**	**935**	**6662**	**7599**

* Not coded in 1987/88   *(a) Environment not coded in 1986/87*

TABLE 40:
cont...

Fatal	1989/90 Major	Over-3-day	Total	Fatal	1990/91 Major	Over-3-day	Total	Fatal	1991/92 Major	Over-3-day	Total
4	219	1935	2158	-	215	2301	2516	2	204	2598	2804
-	237	2024	2261	-	282	2331	2613	-	252	2461	2716
2	99	796	897	-	87	912	999	-	70	904	974
-	127	628	755	1	152	673	826	-	105	668	773
-	34	302	336	-	44	373	417	-	47	421	468
-	31	362	393	-	39	295	334	-	31	269	300
-	30	304	334	-	35	287	322	-	13	257	270
-	9	332	341	-	9	327	336	-	5	264	269
-	22	125	147	-	13	136	149	-	25	231	256
-	25	171	196	-	28	211	239	-	26	202	228
-	26	199	225	-	24	232	256	-	31	188	219
-	16	108	124	-	15	129	144	-	19	147	166
-	25	86	111	-	11	90	101	-	23	115	138
-	17	107	124	-	18	103	121	-	26	102	128
1	35	224	260	-	45	297	342	-	56	410	466
7	952	7703	8662	1	1017	8697	9715	2	933	9237	10172

TABLE 41:

Major injuries to employees (including trainees) in retail distribution as reported to local authorities 1986/87-1991/92

Kind of accident	Number of injuries						Total
	1986/87	1987/88	1988/89	1989/90	1990/91	1991/92	6 years
Slip, trip or fall on same level	340	433	467	438	491	476	2645
Fall from a height	155	175	162	191	184	168	1035
Struck by moving inc. flying/falling object	105	112	83	100	95	70	565
Injured whilst handling, lifting or carrying	52	73	54	61	64	55	359
Struck against something fixed or stationary	63	57	51	48	58	55	332
Struck by moving vehicle	42	61	62	50	54	44	313
Exposure to or contact with harmful substance	13	19	26	30	36	34	158
Contact with moving machinery or material	25	22	22	24	24	15	132
Contact with electricity or electrical discharge	13	9	6	2	2	5	37
Exposure to an explosion	3	1	-	-	-	3	7
Exposure to fire	1	-	-	2	-	1	4
Other kind of accident	2	9	2	6	9	7	35
Total	**814**	**971**	**935**	**952**	**1017**	**933**	**5622**

Incidence rate per 100 000 employees

1986/87	1987/88	1988/89	1989/90	1990/91	1991/92
17.0	21.2	22.0	19.7	22.2	20.6
7.7	8.7	7.8	8.7	8.2	7.6
5.3	5.4	4.0	4.6	4.3	3.0
2.7	3.6	2.7	2.7	2.9	2.5
3.0	2.7	2.4	2.3	2.6	2.4
2.0	2.9	2.9	2.3	2.4	1.9
0.7	1.0	1.3	1.3	1.7	1.5
1.5	1.2	1.3	1.1	1.2	0.7
0.0	0.0	0.0	0.0	0.0	0.2
0.1	0.0	0.0	0.0	0.0	0.1
0.1	0.0	0.0	0.1	0.0	0.0
0.1	0.5	0.2	0.3	0.4	0.3
41.0	**47.6**	**44.7**	**43.2**	**45.9**	**41.0**

TABLE 42:

Over-3-day injuries to employees (including trainees) in retail distribution as reported to local authorities 1986/87-1991/92

Kind of accident	Number of injuries						Total 6 years
	1986/87	1987/88	1988/89	1989/90	1990/91	1991/92	
Injured whilst handling, lifting or carrying	1379	1728	1914	2185	2654	2990	12850
Slip, trip or fall on same level	1141	1349	1571	1825	2190	2177	10253
Struck by moving inc. flying/falling object	980	1025	1123	1249	1334	1415	7126
Struck by moving vehicle	398	594	604	792	799	809	3996
Struck against something fixed or stationary	439	447	458	584	620	636	3184
Fall from a height	434	516	551	615	595	626	3337
Contact with moving machinery or material	155	235	260	259	273	249	1431
Exposure to or contact with harmful substance	82	114	116	113	146	180	751
Contact with electricity or electrical discharge	11	18	19	25	17	39	129
Injured by an animal	10	16	16	21	14	10	87
Exposure to an explosion	3	5	3	1	7	10	29
Drowning or asphyxiation	-	-	-	-	-	4	4
Exposure to fire	1	7	6	2	3	3	22
Trapped by something collapsing or overturning	1	-	-	-	-	-	1
Other kind of accident	25	53	21	32	45	89	265
Total	**5059**	**6107**	**6662**	**7703**	**8697**	**9237**	**43465**

Number of injuries

1986/87	1987/88	1988/89	1989/90	1990/91	1991/92
70.1	85.7	92.1	98.4	119.5	130.8
57.0	65.8	75.3	81.6	98.4	95.2
48.6	50.1	53.6	56.1	60.0	61.9
19.4	28.4	28.5	35.2	35.6	35.2
22.0	22.0	21.9	26.2	27.7	28.0
22.1	25.7	26.7	27.9	27.0	27.5
8.0	11.7	12.6	11.7	12.4	10.9
4.6	5.6	5.6	5.1	6.7	7.8
0.5	0.9	0.7	0.9	0.7	1.7
0.7	0.9	0.9	1.1	0.8	0.4
0.1	0.3	0.2	0.0	0.4	0.4
0.0	0.0	0.0	0.0	0.0	0.2
0.1	0.3	0.3	0.1	0.1	0.1
0.1	0.1	0.1	0.0	0.0	0.0
1.6	3.2	1.3	1.8	2.2	4.1
254.9	**300.6**	**319.8**	**346.1**	**391.4**	**404.1**

TABLE 43:

Injuries investigated in the LA sector for the period 1/4/91 to 31/3/92 : RIDDOR National estimates for Great Britain (grossed up from 404 LAE 1 returns)

	Employed	Public	Total
Cases of injury investigated during the period 1 April 1991 to 31 March 1992	14 170	1880	16 050

TABLE 44:

Other information reported to LAs and LA staff resources 1991/92. National estimates for Great Britain (grossed up from 404 LAE 1 returns)

DISEASE Number of cases of disease reported in 1991/92	43
DANGEROUS OCCURRENCES Number of Dangerous Occurrences reported in 1991/92	333
COMPLAINTS Number of complaints investigated under Health and Safety legislation	21 300
Number of complaints which proved to be unfounded	3 100
STAFF RESOURCES Number of inspectors holding appointments under Section 19 of the HSW Act on 31 March 1992	5920
Full-Time Equivalent number of all professional/technical staff undertaking HSW duties in 1991/92	1360
Number of professional/technical staff working more or less exclusively on HSW duties (30 hours per week, or 80 % of their time)	400

TABLE 45:
Enforcement action. National estimates for Great Britain (grossed up from 404 LAE 1 returns)

FORMAL NOTICES ISSUED DURING 1991/92	
Improvement notices	18 980
Deferred prohibition notices	290
Immediate prohibition notices	2410
Total formal notices issued during 1991/92	**21 680**
LETTERS	
Number of letters, or other informal notices asking for compliance, issued during 1991/92 of which:	138 780
number followed up by formal notice	3170
PROSECUTIONS	
Number of people prosecuted for whom a hearing was completed during 1991/92 Prosecutions taken mainly under:	
Offices, Shops and Railway Premises Act	29
Factories Act	13
Health and Safety at Work Act	374
Regulations	92
Other health and safety legislation	6
Total prosecutions completed during 1991/92	**514**

TABLE 46A:
PROSECUTION BY LOCAL AUTHORITIES BY TYPE OF LEGISLATION: Number of hearings completed during 1991/92 (Based on 404 Returns)

Prosecutions taken under:	ENGLAND AND WALES		SCOTLAND		
	Information	Convictions	Complaints submitted to Procurator Fiscal	Complaints taken by Procurator Fiscal	Convictions
Offices, Shops and Railway Premises Act	48	40	9	4	4
Health and Safety at Work Act	465	418	51	35	26
Factories Act	22	19	5	5	-
Local Authority Act 1990	11	8	-	-	-
Specific Regulations	191	173	5	-	-
Other Legislation	2	2	-	-	-
ALL LEGISLATION	**739**	**660**	**70**	**44**	**30**

TABLE 46B:
PROSECUTION BY LOCAL AUTHORITIES BY TYPE OF OFFENCE: Number of hearings completed during 1991/92 (Based on 404 Returns)

Prosecutions taken under: Offices, Shops and Railway Premises Act		ENGLAND AND WALES		SCOTLAND		
		Information	Convictions	Complaints submitted to Procurator Fiscal	Complaints taken by Procurator Fiscal	Convictions
S.4	Cleanliness	4	4	1	-	-
S.5	Overcrowding	-	-	-	-	-
S.6	Temperature	-	-	-	-	-
S.7	Ventilation	1	1	-	-	-
S.8	Lighting	3	3	2	2	2
S.9	Sanitary conveniences	6	5	1	-	-
S.10	Washing facilities	3	1	-	-	-
S.11	Supply of drinking water	1	-	-	-	-
S.15	Eating facilities	-	-	-	-	-
S.16	Floors, passages and stairs	16	15	5	2	2
S.17	Fencing of exposed parts of machinery	10	8	-	-	-
S.18	Avoidance of exposure of young persons to danger in cleaning machinery	1	1	-	-	-
S.19	Training and supervision of person working at dangerous machines	1	1	-	-	-
S.20	Regulations for securing health and safety (Hoists and Lifts Regulations)	-	-	-	-	-
S.24	First-aid general provisions	-	-	-	-	-
S.33	Safety Provision in case of fire	-	-	-	-	-
S.49	Notification of fact of employment of persons	2	1	-	-	-
S.50	Information for employees	-	-	-	-	-
TOTAL UNDER OFFICES, SHOPS AND RAILWAY PREMISES ACT		**48**	**40**	**9**	**4**	**4**

TABLE 46C:
PROSECUTION BY LOCAL AUTHORITIES BY TYPE OF OFFENCE: *Number of hearings completed during 1991/92 (Based on 404 returns)*

Prosecutions taken under: Health and Safety at Work Act	ENGLAND AND WALES		SCOTLAND		
	Information	Convictions	Complaints submitted to Procurator Fiscal	Complaints taken by Procurator Fiscal	Convictions
S.2 General duties of employers to their employees of which:	281	260	27	16	12
2.1	124	117	13	10	7
2.2	129	119	8	3	3
2.3	18	14	6	3	2
Other	10	10	-	-	-
S.3 General duties of employers and self employed persons other than employees of which:	81	69	6	6	3
3.1	57	49	4	4	2
3.2	12	12	2	1	1
Other	12	8	-	1	-
S.4 General duties of persons concerned with premises to persons other than their employees	13	10	3	2	1
S.6 General duties of manufacturers etc as regards articles and substances at work	1	1	-	-	-
S.7 General duties of employees at work	10	9	2	-	-
S.8 Duty not to interfere with or misuse things provided pursuant to certain provisions	-	-	-	-	-
S.16 Approval of codes of practice by the Commission	2	2			
S.33 Offences	76	66	11	11	10
S.36 Offences due to fault of other person	-	-	1	-	-
S.37 Offences by bodies corporate	1	1	1	-	-
TOTAL UNDER HEALTH AND SAFETY AT WORK ACT	**465**	**418**	**51**	**35**	**26**

TABLE 46D:

PROSECUTION BY LOCAL AUTHORITIES UNDER SPECIFIC REGULATIONS: Number of hearings completed during 1991/92 (Based on 404 returns)

Prosecutions taken under:	ENGLAND AND WALES		SCOTLAND		
	Information	Convictions	Complaints submitted to Procurator Fiscal	Complaints taken by Procurator Fiscal	Convictions
Control of Asbestos at Work	1	1	-	-	-
Electricity	98	86	1	-	-
Health and Safety (First-aid)	3	2	-	-	-
Information for Employees	5	4	1	-	-
RIDDOR	58	56	2	-	-
OSRP - Hoists and Lifts	5	5	-	-	-
Sanitary Conveniences	1	1	-	-	-
Woodworking Machines	2	2	-	-	-
COSHH	18	16	1	-	-
Other	-	-	-	-	-
TOTAL ALL REGULATIONS	**191**	**173**	**5**	**-**	**-**

TABLE 47:

Premises by type of local authority (based on 404 returns)

	Average number of premises per local authority						
	Retail shops	Wholesale, ware-houses	Offices	Catering services	Residential accomm-odation	Consumer /leisure services	All premises
Great Britain (404)	980	150	490	400	160	370	2650
London Boroughs (28)	1820	270	1630	810	410	920	5790
Metropolitan Districts (32)	2550	440	1070	720	100	810	5730
Urban and Industrial (83)	1020	140	460	380	110	290	2420
Suburban (118)	660	130	340	290	60	280	1940
Resort and Retirement (28)	1110	120	410	520	680	420	3150
Rural (60)	690	90	230	400	190	320	1950
Scottish Urban (24)	830	120	430	350	50	270	2580
Scottish Rural (31)	390	40	160	140	120	180	1020

Figures in brackets refer to the number of returns in each category.

TABLE 48:

Employed persons and number of visits by type of local authority (based on 404 returns)

	Average number per local authority of:		
	Employed persons in the LA sector	General HSW inspections	Total visits
Great Britain (404)	15 400	570	1130
London Boroughs (28)	53 700	760	2180
Metropolitan Districts(32)	32 300	1100	2470
Urban and Industrial (83)	14 200	590	1120
Suburban (118)	12 500	450	830
Resort and Retirement (28)	15 200	540	1270
Rural (60)	6700	440	700
Scottish Urban (24)	11 700	940	1670
Scottish Rural (31)	4100	300	440

Figures in brackets refer to the number of returns in each category.

TABLE 49:

Complaints, staff and enforcement activity by type of local authority (based on 404 returns)

	Average number per local authority of:				
	Complaints investigated under HSW legislation	Full-Time equivalent no of profess-ional or technical staff	Formal notices issued	Letters asking for compliance issued	Prosecutions completed
Great Britain (404)	45	3	48	305	1
London Boroughs (28)	155	6	77	181	3
Metropolitan Districts (32)	108	6	154	487	5
Urban and Industrial (83)	41	3	66	333	1
Suburban (118)	30	2	27	221	1
Resort and Retirement (28)	51	3	31	414	1
Rural (60)	20	2	21	257	-
Scottish Urban (24)	44	4	44	639	1
Scottish Rural (31)	7	1	7	195	-

A dash (-) indicates figure is less than 0.5

Figures in brackets refer to the number of returns in each category.

TABLE 50:

Changes in visits made since 1986/87

| Type of premises | Change in number of visits made between 1986/87 and 1991/92 | | Total visits made 1991/92 |
	General inspections	All visits	
Consumer/leisure services	+ 19 %	+ 46 %	74 000
Offices	- 46 %	- 34 %	47 000
Retail shops	- 30 %	- 21 %	187 000
Wholesale, warehouses, etc	- 26 %	+ 3 %	37 000
Residential accommodation	- 12 %	level	31 000
Catering services	- 8 %	+ 12 %	136 000
All premises	- 19 %	- 8 %	512 000

Estimates for 1991/92 grossed up from 404 LAE 1 forms.

APPENDIX FOUR:

List of local authorities that returned the LAE 1 form for 1991/92 (404 in all)

We would like to thank these LAs for their co-operation.

COUNTY	LOCAL AUTHORITY
AVON	Bath; Bristol; Kingswood; Northavon; Wansdyke; Woodspring
BEDFORDSHIRE	North Bedfordshire; Luton; Mid Bedfordshire; South Bedfordshire
BERKSHIRE	Bracknell Forest; Reading; Slough; Windsor and Maidenhead
BUCKINGHAMSHIRE	Aylesbury Vale; South Buckinghamshire; Chiltern; Milton Keynes; Wycombe
CAMBRIDGESHIRE	Cambridge; East Cambridgeshire; Fenland; Huntingdonshire; Peterborough
CHESHIRE	Crewe and Nantwich; Ellesmere Port and Neston; Vale Royal; Warrington
CLEVELAND	Hartlepool; Langbaurgh-on-Tees; Middlesbrough; Stockton-on-Tees
CORNWALL	Caradon; Kerrier; North Cornwall; Penwith; Restormel
CUMBRIA	Allerdale; Barrow-in-Furness; Carlisle; Copeland; Eden; South Lakeland
DERBYSHIRE	Amber Valley; Bolsover; Chesterfield; Derby; Erewash; High Peak; North East Derbyshire; South Derbyshire; Derbyshire Dales
DEVON	Exeter; Plymouth; South Hams; Teignbridge; Mid Devon; Torbay; West Devon
DORSET	Bournemouth; North Dorset; Poole; Purbeck; West Dorset; East Dorset

DURHAM	Chester-le-Street; Darlington; Derwentside; Durham; Easington; Sedgefield; Teesdale; Wear Valley
EAST SUSSEX	Brighton; Eastbourne; Hastings;Hove; Lewes; Rother; Wealden
ESSEX	Basildon; Braintree; Brentwood; Castle Point; Chelmsford; Colchester; Harlow; Maldon; Rochford; Southend-on-Sea; Tendring; Thurrock; Uttlesford
GLOUCESTERSHIRE	Cheltenham; Cotswold; Shroud; Tewkesbury
HAMPSHIRE	Basingstoke and Deane; East Hampshire; Eastleigh; Fareham; Gosport; Hart; Havant; New Forest; Portsmouth; Rushmoor; Test Valley; Winchester
HEREFORD AND WORCESTER	Bromsgrove; Hereford; Leominster; Redditch; South Herefordshire; Worcester; Wychavon; Wyre Forest
HERTFORDSHIRE	Broxbourne; Dacorum; East Hertfordshire; Hertsmere; North Hertfordshire; St Albans; Three Rivers; Watford; Welwyn Hatfield
HUMBERSIDE	Beverley; Boothferry; Cleethorpes; Glanford; Great Grimsby; Holderness; Kingston-upon-Hull; East Yorkshire; Scunthorpe
ISLE OF WIGHT	Medina; South Wight
KENT	Ashford; Castlebury; Dartford; Dover; Gillingham; Gravesham; Rochester-upon-Medway; Sevenoaks; Shepway; Thanet; Tonbridge and Malling; Tunbridge Wells; Swale
LANCASHIRE	Blackburn; Blackpool; Burnley; Chorley; Hyndburn; Pendle; Preston; Ribble Valley; Rossendale; South Ribble; West Lancashire; Wyre
LEICESTERSHIRE	Blaby; Harborough; Melton; North West Leicestershire; Oadby and Wigston; Rutland
LINCOLNSHIRE	Boston; East Lindsey; Lincoln; North Kesteven; South Holland ; South Kesteven; West Lindsey
NORFOLK	Breckland; Great Yarmouth; Norwich; South Norfolk; Kings Lynn and West Norfolk
NORTH YORKSHIRE	Craven; Hambleton; Harrogate; Richmondshire; Ryedale; Scarborough; Selby; York

NORTHAMPTONSHIRE	Corby; Daventry; East Northamptonshire; Kettering; Northampton; South Northamptonshire; Wellingborough
NORTHUMBERLAND	Alnwick; Blyth Valley; Castle Morpeth
NOTTINGHAMSHIRE	Bassetlaw; Broxtowe; Gedling; Mansfield; Nottingham; Rushcliffe
OXFORDSHIRE	Cherwell; Oxford; South Oxfordshire; Vale of White Horse; West Oxfordshire
SHROPSHIRE	Bridgnorth; Taunton Deane; Oswestry; Shrewsbury and Atcham
SOMERSET	Sedgemoor; West Somerset ; South Somerset
STAFFORDSHIRE	East Staffordshire; Lichfield; Newcastle-under-Lyme; Stafford; South Staffordshire; Staffordshire Moorlands; Stoke-on-Trent; Tamworth
SUFFOLK	Babergh; Forest Heath; Ipswich; Mid Suffolk; St Edmundsbury; Suffolk Coastal; Waveney
SURREY	Elmbridge; Epsom and Ewell; Guildford; Mole Valley; Reigate and Banstead; Runnymede; Spelthorne; Surrey Heath; Tandridge; Waverley; Woking
WARWICKSHIRE	North Warwickshire; Nuneaton and Bedworth; Rugby; Stratford-upon-Avon; Warwick
WEST SUSSEX	Adur; Arun; Chichester; Horsham; Mid Sussex
WILTSHIRE	Kennet; North Wiltshire; Salisbury; Thamesdown
GREATER MANCHESTER	Bury; Manchester; Oldham; Rochdale; Salford; Stockport; Tameside; Trafford; Wigan
MERSEYSIDE	Liverpool; St Helens; Sefton; Wirral
SOUTH YORKSHIRE	Barnsley; Doncaster; Rotherham; Sheffield
TYNE AND WEAR	Gateshead; Newcastle-upon-Tyne; South Tyneside; Sunderland
WEST MIDLANDS	Coventry; Dudley; Sandwell; Solihull; Walsall; Wolverhampton
WEST YORKSHIRE	Bradford; Calderdale; Kirklees; Leeds; Wakefield
GREATER LONDON	Corporation of London; Barking and Dagenham; Barnet; Bexley; Brent; Bromley; Camden; Croydon; Ealing; Enfield; Hackney; Hammersmith and Fulham; Harrow; Havering; Hillingdon; Hounslow; Islington;

GREATER LONDON cont...	Kensington and Chelsea; Kingston-upon-Thames; Lambeth; Merton; Newham; Redbridge; Southwark; Sutton; Waltham Forest; Wandsworth; Westminster
CLWYD	Alyn and Deeside; Colwyn; Delyn; Glyndwr; Rhuddlan
DYFED	Carmarthen; Llanelli; Preseli Pembrokeshire; South Pembrokeshire
GWENT	Blaenau Gwent; Islwyn; Monmouth; Newport; Torfaen
GWYNEDD	Aberconwy; Dwyfor; Meirionnydd; Ynys Mon - Isle of Anglesey
MID GLAMORGAN	Cynon Valley; Merthyr Tydfil; Ogwr; Rhondda; Rhymney Valley; Taff-Ely
POWYS	Brecknock; Montgomeryshire; Radnor
SOUTH GLAMORGAN	Cardiff; Vale of Glamorgan
WEST GLAMORGAN	Port Talbot; Lliw Valley; Neath; Swansea
BORDERS	Berwickshire; Ettrick and Lauderdale; Roxburgh; Tweedale
CENTRAL	Clackmannan; Falkirk; Stirling
DUMFRIES AND GALLOWAY	Annandale and Eskdale; Wigtown; Nithsdale; Stewartry
FIFE	Dunfermline; Kirkcaldy; North East Fife
GRAMPIAN	Aberdeen; Banff and Buchan; Gordon; Kincardine and Deeside; Moray
HIGHLAND	Badenoch and Strathspey; Caithness; Inverness; Lochaber; Nairn; Ross and Cromerty; Skye and Lochalsh; Sutherland
LOTHIAN	East Lothian; Edinburgh; Midlothian; West Lothian
STRATHCLYDE	Argyll and Bute; Bearsden and Milngavie; Strathkelvin; Clydebank; Cumnock and Doon Valley; Cunninghame; Dumbarton; East Kilbride; Eastwood; Glasgow; Hamilton; Inverclyde; Kilmarnock and Loudoun; Kyle and Carrick; Clydesdale; Monklands; Motherwell; Renfrew
TAYSIDE	Angus; Dundee; Perth and Kinross
ORKNEY	
SHETLAND	
WESTERN ISLES	

APPENDIX FIVE

Enforcement arrangements and responsibilities

LOCAL AUTHORITIES

1. District councils are responsible for the majority of the health and safety enforcement work allocated to local authorities. There are 461 district councils who are enforcing authorities under the HSW Act, including the London Boroughs, Metropolitan Districts and the three Scottish Islands Councils. Health and safety enforcement is usually carried out by Environmental Health Departments or departments responsible for the environmental health function and 5920 inspectors were authorised by local authorities to enforce the Act. Many of these inspectors have other responsibilities relating to food safety, environmental protection, housing and other environmental health work. However, 400 inspectors work exclusively on HSW Act duties and the full time equivalent number of qualified staff employed on HSW Act work is 1360.

2. In addition to the principal role of district councils, county councils in England and Wales and regional councils in Scotland have responsibilities under certain relevant statutory provisions, such as those relating to petroleum licensing and some explosives, including fireworks. They also have responsibilities under some regulations made under the HSW Act, such as the packaging and labelling of dangerous substances, in consumer premises. Forty-seven county councils in England and Wales and nine regional councils in Scotland have these responsibilities which are carried out by Trading Standards Officers or by the Fire Authorities, as appropriate. London boroughs, Metropolitan Districts and Scottish Islands Councils are also responsible for consumer protection and some of the county functions fall to them and are often carried out in combined Environmental Health and Consumer Protection Departments.

3. The premises where local authorities are responsible for enforcing health and safety legislation are determined by the Health and Safety (Enforcing Authority) Regulations. Prior to 1 April 1990, under the 1977 Regulations, LAs were responsible for enforcement in just over one million premises, including shops, offices, warehouses, hotels and catering premises.

4. During the year 1990/91 the Health and Safety (Enforcing Authority) Regulations 1989 were approved by the Secretary of State. It is estimated that from 1 April 1990 these Regulations have re-allocated about 120 000 additional premises to local authorities for enforcement. These include: leisure and consumer services; churches and places of religious worship; the care, treatment and accommodation of animals and certain lower risk construction work carried out in premises where LAs enforce the HSW Act. These Regulations are also designed to remove certain anomalies and to clarify areas of demarcation between HSE and LA inspectors. They should ensure that most businesses will have to deal with only one enforcing authority for health and safety matters.

5. The Regulations simplify the procedure, in cases of uncertainty, for assignment of premises by the Health and Safety Commission (HSC) to an enforcing authority. The procedures for the transfer of enforcement responsibility for particular premises are also simplified. This can now be done administratively by agreement between the enforcing authorities.

6   To promote consistency in enforcement, HELA issues published guidance to LAs and also Local Authority Circulars (LACs) which give advice on general enforcement policy and on particular enforcement problems. These advise on the arrangements and organisation necessary for effective inspection; the impact, scope and interpretation of health and safety legislation; and matters such as machinery guarding and the control of various hazards. These technical circulars often incorporate a datasheet which may be handed to employers during visits. Technical guidance is drawn up and issued by HSE's Local Authority Unit (LAU) in consultation with other parts of HSE, individual LAs, members of HELA and industry as appropriate.

APPENDIX 6:

Health and Safety Executive/Local Authority Enforcement Liaison Committee (HELA)

HELA brings together representatives and professional advisers of the Local Authority Associations and officials of HSE and other relevant organisations. Local authorities are represented by the following associations:

> The Association of County Councils (ACC)
>
> The Association of District Councils (ADC)
>
> The Association of Metropolitan Authorities (AMA)
>
> The Convention of Scottish Local Authorities (COSLA)

The committee provides a forum for discussion and exchange of information on a wide range of health and safety issues. It seeks to achieve a consistent approach to enforcement of health and safety legislation, across local authorities and between HSE and local authorities. It is jointly chaired by Dr J McQuaid, Director of HSE's Strategy and General Division, and Mr W G Myers, Director of the Environment Department at the London Borough of Hammersmith and Fulham.

Much of the work for which HELA is responsible is handled by five sub-committees; SCHELA (Standards of Compliance), SHELA (Statistics), THELA (Training), EUROHELA (European matters) and PHELA (Pesticides). The sub-committees report to HELA, which approves their work programmes. Reports on the work of these sub-committees can be found in paragraphs 6-32.

The Local Authority Unit (LAU) of HSE, provides the secretariat for the HELA committee structure. Details of HELA's plan of work for 1993/94 are given at paragraph 190.

Local authorities' approach to enforcement

The following explanation of the approach by local authorities to the enforcement of health and safety legislation has been prepared by a Working Group of the Health and Safety Executive/Local Authority Enforcement Liaison Committee (HELA). HELA endorses the statement and commends it to all local authorities as a model for their own enforcement statement:

1   The primary responsibility for ensuring health and safety in the workplace lies with those who create the risks, and in particular employers need to recognise their responsibility for managing health and safety.

2   Local authorities' approach to enforcement reflects the responsibilities laid upon them by the 1974 Health and Safety at Work etc Act and the range of powers that that Act made available. The types of premises and activites where local authorities enforce is determined by the Health and Safety (Enforcing Authority) Regulations 1989.

3   Depending on particular circumstances, local authorities may use a variety of means to ensure that employers meet their responsibilities including education, advice, guidance, warning letters, improvement and prohibition notices or prosecutions. Local authorities will generally reserve prosecutions (and therefore criminal proceedings) for the more serious offences which either result or could have resulted in serious injury or ill-health or which represented a blatant disregard by employers, employees, or others of their responsibilities under health and safety legislation.

ENFORCING HEALTH AND SAFETY LAW

4   Local authority enforcement officers' primary concern is the prevention of accidents and ill-health. This is best achieved by encouraging effective management of health and safety by those who create the risks. Enforcement officers seek to help businesses improve their management of health and safety by giving guidance on prevention. They are a source of help on how best to maintain good standards in conformity with the law, and their guidance is usually followed.

5   Enforcement officers have to exercise considerable discretion when approaching individual employers. Most employers are, in local authorities' experience, anxious to comply with the law and a growing number realise the economic benefits of good health and safety management. In such cases an enforcement officer's role will often be to guide and support. However, in carrying out their functions, duly authorised enforcement officers have a range of powers, and may, for example, in certain circumstances take possession of articles or substances; and may ask for articles to be dismantled or subjected to tests. If enforcement officers find evidence that the law is being broken they can respond in various ways. They may instruct or warn by letter, they may issue a prohibition or improvement notice requiring immediate compliance or compliance within a certain specified time, or they may prosecute. Notices are effective and quick and require employers to put dangerous situations right, without the delay and uncertainty of going to court. For these reasons enforcement officers issue a number of notices every year. However, if the circumstances warrant it, they will prosecute without any prior warnings and without any recourse to alternative sanctions.

PROSECUTION TO ENSURE PREVENTION

6   In keeping with its preventive role, a local authority may use prosecution as a way to draw attention to the need for compliance and the maintenance of good standards. Enforcement officers investigating breaches of the law consider their potential to cause harm as well as any harm actually caused. Thus a local authority may seek prosecution if a breach has significant potential for harm, regardless of whether it caused an injury.

7   In deciding whether to prosecute, a local authority will also consider:

- the gravity of the offence;

- the general record and approach of the offender;

- whether it is desirable to be seen to produce some public effect, including the need to ensure remedial action and, through the punishment of offenders, to deter others from similar failures to comply with the law;

- whether the evidence available provides a realistic prospect of conviction. (In this respect a local authority is guided by the Code for Crown Prosecutors published by the Crown Prosecution Service.)

8   In England and Wales the decision to proceed with a court case rests with the local authority itself. In Scotland the Procurator Fiscal decides.

THE PROSECUTION OF INDIVIDUALS

9   Sections 7, 36 and 37 of HSW Act allow for the prosecution of individuals who have committed a health and safety offence. Local authorities' policy is to identify and prosecute individuals if a conviction is warranted and can be secured, but a health and safety offence is often the result of the negligent or ignorant acts of more than one person. This means it is difficult to prove a link between some incidents and individual directors, managers and employees. However, a local authority may still have the option of taking a case against a company instead of a named individual, and will seek to do so where the circumstances justify it.

PENALTIES

10   Penalties need to be commensurate with offences and the Robens report (Safety and Health at Work (Cmnd. 5034 1972)) made the point that enforcement required stiff penalties. The Offshore Safety Act 1992 made more stringent health and safety penalties available to Magistrates, Crown Courts and their Scottish equivalents. In particular, breach of the core responsibilities set out in sections 2 to 6 of HSWA now attracts a £20 000 maximum fine on summary conviction. The importance of the enforcement notice was reinforced by providing a penalty of a £20 000 fine or six months imprisonment, or both, for non-compliance. (The new penalties structure is outlined in the table below)

PENALTIES FOR CONVICTION UNDER THE HEALTH AND SAFETY AT WORK ETC ACT 1974 (HSWA) AND RELEVANT STATUTORY PROVISIONS

Offences heard only in the lower penalty courts	Maximum
Breach of section 14 of HSWA, concerning the power of the HSC to direct investigations and inquiries	
Preventing or attempting to prevent any person from appearing before or answering any question put by an inspector (section 20(2) HSWA)	£5000 for offences committed on or after 1.10.92
obstructing an inspector	
impersonating an inspector	

Offences which can be heard in all courts	Maximum penalties in the lower courts
Breach of HSWA not specified below, or of relevant statutory provisions under HSWA.	£5000 for offences committed on or after 1.10.92
Breach of sections 2 to 6 of HSWA	£20 000 for offences committed on or after 6.3.92
Breach of improvement, prohibition or court remedy order	£20 000 or 6 months imprisonment, or both for offences committed on or after 6.3.92

Offences which can be heard in all courts	Maximum penalties in the higher courts
Breach of HSWA not specified below, or of relevant statutory provisions under HSWA.	unlimited fine
Breach of prohibition order	unlimited fine, or two years' imprisonment, or both
Breach of an improvement order or court remedy order	unlimited fine, or two years' imprisonment, or or both for offences committed on or after 6.3.92
Breach of a licence's terms and conditions or doing something without a licence for which one is necessary	unlimited fine, or two years' imprisonment, or both
Breach of any of the relevant statutory provisions concerning the acquisition, possession or use of an explosive article or substance	

NOTES

1   The daily fine (previously in HSWA s33(5)) has been abolished.

2   There are a small number of offences in older relevant statutory provisions which attract a fixed penalty. As regulations are revised these penalties will be brought into line with the majority.

CONSISTENCY OF ENFORCEMENT STANDARDS BETWEEN LOCAL AUTHORITIES AND HSE AND BETWEEN INDIVIDUAL LOCAL AUTHORITIES

11   National arrangements exist through the Health and Safety Executive/Local Authority Enforcement Liaison Committee (HELA) for coordination on enforcement standards between local authorities and the Health and Safety Executive and between individual local authorities. HELA provides a forum for the development of consistent national advice and training for all local authorities on enforcement issues and for the production of industry specific guidance. It prepares an annual report to the Health and Safety Commission on behalf of all local authorities who enforce the Health and Safety at Work Act. This report is published through HMSO and provides local authorities with information about national trends in accidents in different industry sectors which enables them to target their enforcement resources to the areas of highest risk.

12   Every effort is made to ensure consistent enforcement standards between local authorities. However, local circumstances may preclude an entirely uniform approach on all issues, for example, differences in the mix of risks in employment may lead to different inspection priorities being adopted by individual local authorities.

References

1   HSE *Shopping trolleys: safe system of work guidance* HS(G)84 HMSO 1992 ISBN 0 11 886326 6

2   HSE *Health and safety in retail and wholesale warehouses* HS(G)76 HMSO 1992 ISBN 0 11 885731 2

3   HSE *Successful health and safety management* HS(G)65 HMSO 1991 ISBN 0 11 885988 9

4   HSE *The prevention or control of Legionellosis (including Legionnaire's Disease).* Approved Code of Practice L8 HMSO 1991 ISBN 0 11 885659 6

5   HSE *The control of Legionellosis including Legionnaire's Disease* HS(G)70 HMSO 1991 ISBN 0 11 885660 X

6   HSE video *Dangerous manoeuvres.* Available from CFL Vision PO Box 35 Wetherby LS23 7EX Tel: 0937 541 010

7   HSE *Safety in working with lift trucks* HS(G)6 HMSO (rev ed) 1992 ISBN 0 11 886395 9

8   HSE *Road Transport in factories and similar workplaces* GS9 HMSO (rev ed) 1992 ISBN 0 11 885732 0

9   HSE *Rider operated lift trucks operator training* Approved Code of Practice and supplementary guidance COP 26 HMSO 1988 ISBN 0 11 885459 3

10 HSE *Essentials of health and safety at work* HMSO (rev ed) 1990 ISBN 0 11 885445 3

11 HSE *Safety in the stacking of materials* HSW47 HMSO 1971 ISBN 0 11 880839 7

12 HSE S*afe use of ladders, step ladders and trestles* GS 31 HMSO 1984 ISBN 0 11 883594 7

13 HSC/Sports Council *Safety in swimming pools* 1988 ISBN 0 906577 837 Available from the Sports Council; Publications Department, 16 Upper Woburn Place, London WC1H 0QP Tel: 071 388 1277

14 HSE *Safety in meat preparation: guidance for butchers* HSG(45) HMSO 1988 ISBN 0 11 885461 5